Roads
to Everywhere

By

David H. Russell

Doris Gates

and

Constance M. McCullough

Ginn and Company

Boston · New York · Chicago · Atlanta · Dallas · Columbus
San Francisco · Toronto · London

ILLUSTRATIONS BY

Clare Bice   Else Bostelmann
Mary Highsmith   Forrest Orr
Joan Esley   C. L. Hartman
Leon Berthold   Jonathan Swanson
Ray Quigley   Kurt Wiese

Acknowledgments

Grateful acknowledgment is made to the following authors and publishers for permission to use and adapt copyrighted materials:

Coward-McCann, Inc. for "The Five Chinese Brothers," adapted from *The Five Chinese Brothers* by Claire Huchet Bishop and Kurt Wiese, copyright 1938, by Coward-McCann, Inc.

Doubleday & Company, Inc. for "Vegetables" from *Taxis and Toadstools* by Rachel Field, copyright 1926, by Doubleday & Company, Inc.; and for "If Only" from *Gay Go Up* by Rose Fyleman, copyright 1929, 1930, by Doubleday & Company, Inc.

E. P. Dutton & Company, Inc. for "The Secret Cave," adapted from *The Secret Cave* by Florence McClurg Everson and Howard Everson, published and copyright by E. P. Dutton & Company, Inc.

Katherine W. Eyre and *Trails for Juniors* for "Janie's Thanksgiving."

Follett Publishing Company for "Pussy Willows" from *Around a Toadstool Table* by Rowena Bastin Bennett; and for "Animals' Eyes," adapted from *The World of Animals* by Mary Bowen Stephenson.

Harcourt, Brace and Company, Inc. for "Success for Little Blacknose," adapted from *Little Blacknose* by Hildegarde Hoyt Swift, copyright 1929, by Harcourt, Brace and Company, Inc.

Holiday House, Inc. for "Flipper," adapted from *Flipper, a Sea Lion* by Irma S. Black.

Henry Holt and Company, Inc. for "Someone" from "Peacock Pie" in *Collected Poems* by Walter de la Mare, copyright 1920, by Henry Holt and Company, Inc.

J. B. Lippincott Company for "The Horseless Carriage" from *Father's Big Improvements* by Caroline D. Emerson, copyright 1936, by J. B. Lippincott Company; and for "The First Lamb" from *Children of North Africa* by Louise Stinetorf.

Little, Brown & Company for "Eletelephony" from *Tirra Lirra* by Laura E. Richards; reprinted by permission of Little, Brown & Company.

Longmans, Green and Company for "Pedro's House" from *Pedro's Coconut Skates* by Esther Wood.

The Macmillan Company for "When Totaram Washed the Elephant" from *Totaram* by Irene Mott Bose; for "Roads" from *Pointed People* by Rachel Field; for "Digger, Prairie Mole" from *Prairie Neighbors* by Edith M. Patch and Carroll Lane Fenton; and for "Way Ping, Master of Boats" from *Rabbit Lantern* by Dorothy Rowe; all by permission of The Macmillan Company, publishers.

Rinehart & Company, Inc. for "Kintu," adapted from *Kintu: A Congo Adventure* by Elizabeth Enright, copyright 1935, by Elizabeth Enright Gilham, and reprinted by permission of Rinehart & Company, Inc., Publishers.

3

4

Contents

Daring Deeds

Neighbors Round the World

Moving On

Old Favorites

Animals We Like

They Earned Their Way

Exploring Nature's Secrets

Fun and Nonsense

Daring Deeds

The Secret Cave

A Young Explorer

When Sammy Andy was ten years old, his uncle gave him a flashlight. The present made Sammy very happy because for a long time he had wanted to do some exploring. Everyone knows that you can't do much exploring without a flashlight. Not if you want to explore a cave anyway! And that is just what Sammy wanted to do.

Sammy lived with his grandfather and grandmother on a farm. He had found the cave one day with Rex, the farm dog. They had gone along the brook that ran out of a hillside on the farm. There Sammy had found the cave.

Rex had found it first. Rex had gone sniffing under some rocks, and Sammy had become interested.

When Sammy got down and put his face close to the rocks, he had felt a cold breath of air. Where was the cold air coming from, he had wondered.

10

So Sammy had moved away some of the rocks and had found the tiny opening to the cave. By digging away a few more rocks, he had been able to wiggle into the cave. Rex had wiggled in right behind him.

They had stood very close together in the cold darkness of the cave for several minutes, not making a sound. It wasn't that Sammy was really afraid, but just sort of surprised. He had felt, all of a sudden, very glad to have Rex along. After a few minutes he and Rex had wiggled back into the sunshine.

From that day the wish to explore the cave had filled Sammy's thoughts. But he knew it would be a very foolish deed without a flashlight. And he didn't have a flashlight.

Whenever he said that he wanted one, someone was sure to ask, "What in the world do you want a flashlight for?" But Sammy did not want to say anything about the cave. It was his secret. A secret cave was fun to think about.

Now, a year later, Sammy had his flashlight. He could hardly wait for the next Saturday when he would have his first chance to explore the cave.

Saturday came at last, and right after breakfast Sammy packed a lunch and set out. Rex was waiting for him, and they went off together. After a while they came to the foot of the hills and to the opening of the secret cave.

Sammy moved away the stones which hid the opening, and he and Rex wiggled in. As soon as they were on the other side, Sammy pressed the button of his flashlight. Then he was surprised. The cave was large, and its walls were wet and shiny.

12

In the back wall there was a deep crack, and out of it ran a little stream. It ran across the cave and under the front wall. Sammy knew it was the same little brook he had followed in coming to the cave. He walked toward it slowly. His steps rang out loudly in the cave. The hair along Rex's back was standing straight up.

Sammy stood for a long time thinking, with his flashlight held on the deep crack in the wall.

There must be another cave on the other side of the wall, he thought. A brook couldn't just come out of nowhere. Perhaps if he could dig out some of the wall around the stream bed, he would dare to crawl under there, too.

Putting down the flashlight very gently, Sammy began digging along the banks of the brook. It was easy digging, for the stream bed was smooth sand.

But Sammy didn't have much luck in making the bed larger. As fast as he dug out a little of it, the water spread out and filled it in again. At last he had to give it up. With his flashlight he explored the back wall to find another crack.

Surprises

Just then there was a loud crash. What was that noise? Sammy turned his light toward the sound, and then he saw what had made it.

In digging at the stream bed, he had dug away some of the sand on which the rocks of the back wall were resting. As the stream had washed away the sand, the rocks had settled down. One large rock near the roof had crashed from the wall to the floor, leaving a hole like a window.

Sammy climbed up and held his flashlight to the hole. What a sight met his eyes then!

Sparkling and twinkling in the light were beautiful pink walls and strange, rocky posts. And the cave seemed to stretch for miles and miles into darkness. Long pieces of twinkling pink stone hung from the top of the cave, and it all looked like fairyland.

14

Now Sammy felt just like an explorer. He was sure that no other eyes but his had ever gazed upon this sight, and he wanted to explore the place some more. He began crawling through the opening. It wasn't easy with his flashlight in one hand and his lunch in the other. But he got there at last.

The only trouble was that Rex would not follow him. He stood whining in the dark on the other side of the wall.

"Here, Rex," called Sammy. "Come on, old boy." But Rex did not come. Perhaps he was cold, or he didn't like the darkness.

At last Sammy called, "All right, Rex. Go on home." But he wished the dog would stay with him.

After a while Sammy didn't hear Rex whining any more. So he decided that the good dog's nose had led him to the opening of the cave and the sunlight outside.

Sammy walked ahead slowly, holding the flashlight out in front of him. The bottom of the cave was hard rock, and every footstep he took made a loud, hollow sound. At his feet the little brook went smoothly and quietly along.

For three whole minutes, Sammy walked along carefully. He was just beginning to feel at home in this strange place when all at once his eyes fell upon something that stopped him right in his tracks.

His heart began to beat very fast, and the flashlight shook a little in his hands. There in the sand beside the brook were two footprints! They were large footprints and had been made by a man. Sammy gazed at them with wonder.

Just when they had been pressed into the sand he could not tell. One thing was sure, he was not the first person who had looked upon this place. Someone had been here before him. Perhaps that person was hiding in the cave now!

16

All at once Sammy was scared. He forgot all about wanting to be an explorer. He just wanted to get out of the cave as quickly as he could.

Turning, he ran as fast as he could back along the way he had come. He raced over the wet rocks, with the flashlight swinging wildly. Then he caught his toe and fell. The flashlight slipped out of his hand and went bang upon the cave floor. The next second, Sammy was in darkness.

For a minute he couldn't move or think. Then he began to feel around for the flashlight. At last his fingers touched it, and he pressed the button. But there was no light! The flashlight must have broken when it hit the rock floor.

"Now what shall I do?" Sammy asked himself. It was terribly dark—darker than midnight.

Sammy knew it would be foolish to try to find his way out of the cave, because since his fall he wasn't even sure which way he should take. If he tried to find his way out, he might just keep getting deeper and deeper into the hillside.

There was only one thing to do. He must settle down and stay right in this spot until he was found, whenever that might be! It wasn't a very happy thought. If Sammy hadn't been a real explorer, he might have started to yell and cry. But Sammy was brave.

Anyway a thought had come to make him feel better. Rex knew where he was. There was just the chance that Rex might lead someone to the cave to rescue him.

There, alone and lost in the dark, Sammy even began to feel brave and excited as he thought about being rescued. It surely was like being a real explorer to have someone come to your rescue. If only Rex would remember the cave and bring someone back with him before too long!

Rescue

And Rex did remember. When it got toward
dinner time and still no hungry boy came
banging into the kitchen, Grandmother began
hunting for Sammy.

When she didn't find him, she looked around
for Rex. Then she saw that Rex looked at her
in a queer way. Whenever she asked, "Where's
Sammy?" the dog would whine and look worried.
So Grandmother began to worry too. She went
to look for Grandfather.

Grandfather called John, who helped on the farm, and the two of them set out to hunt for Sammy. Rex trotted ahead of them. He led them straight to the brook and along it, until they came at last to where it ran out of the hillside. Here Rex stopped and looked up at Grandfather and whined.

"Well, well," Grandfather said, "I wonder why he brought us up here. Sammy couldn't have gone into the hillside!"

But Rex knew that was just what Sammy had done. So he began sniffing at the little hole where he and Sammy had wiggled into the cave.

Then Grandfather got down and put his face close to the hole. The next minute he was throwing rocks to one side. Soon he had made a big enough opening so that he could crawl through. Then he, too, was standing in Sammy's secret cave with Rex beside him.

"Sammy!" called Grandfather, "Sam-my!"

From far away came an answering shout, "Here, Grandfather. I'm in here."

Then Grandfather shouted, "Stay—right— where—you—are."

20

Grandfather shouted very slowly, so the echo of each word would have ended before the next word came along. "I'm going—to get—a lantern. —I'll come—right back."

"All right," Sammy yelled back, and an echo answered, "All right."

In a little while Sammy saw the lighted lantern bobbing toward him, and there were Grandfather and John. Sammy was so glad to see them that he was even glad when Grandfather first hugged him, then scolded, "Why didn't you tell us where you were going?"

"It was a secret," Sammy said, "but I'll never do it again. It's no fun being lost in the dark, even if you are an explorer."

"A good explorer always leaves word about where he's going," said Grandfather. "And he never, never goes digging under rocks without finding out if it's safe. What if some of those big rocks had fallen on top of you!"

When Sammy thought about that, his knees felt terribly weak. "I'll remember," he promised.

Then he told about the footprints, and with the lantern they went back to see them.

"I have a feeling that they were made in early times by the cave men who must have lived here then," Grandfather said. "Let's go farther and see what we can see."

So the three of them walked on for about half a mile. Then they really did have a surprise!

All over the floor were stones that had been made into hammers, and many small chips of red stone. Here and there among the red stone chips were arrowheads and stone dishes and bowls. In a covered jar were some bright-colored beads.

"These things were made by men in very, very early days," said Grandfather. "They must have lived and worked in this cave long before white men came to this country. Tomorrow we'll call up Mr. Black at the museum and ask him to come down here to see the cave. I'm sure he'll be glad to have these things for the museum."

That made Sammy feel like a real explorer all right. And after all, wasn't he really one? He had found the cave, and so these old treasures were brought to light, and would be in the museum for everyone to see.

Florence and *Howard Everson*

If Only . . .

If only I'd some money,
  I'd buy a jolly boat
And get a pair of sea boots
  And a furry sort of coat,
A case or two of salted beef
  And a seaman's wooden chest,
And I'd sail away to the North Pole,
Or I'd sail away to the South Pole,
  Whichever I thought was best.

I'd get up very early—
    They wouldn't see me go—
Jimmy would be with me,
    But no one else would know.
Dogs are very useful,
    And I couldn't part with Jim,
And whether I went to the North Pole,
Or whether I went to the South Pole,
    It would be all the same to him.

Perhaps we'd see a mountain
    That no one else had seen;
Perhaps we'd find a country
    Where no one else had been.
Suppose we climbed an iceberg
    And saw the midnight sun!
Oh, whether we went to the North Pole,
Or whether we went to the South Pole,
    Wouldn't it all be fun?

Rose Fyleman

Janie's Thanksgiving

Danger

"Janie! Janie! Indians in the cornfield! Hurry, child!"

At the sound of her mother's excited voice, ten-year-old Janie dropped her fishing pole and scampered up the bank of the brook. "Oh-h-h, oh-h-h!" she kept crying as she ran swiftly toward the cabin.

25

In and out among the trees she went, and around huge stones, nearly falling time and again. "Indians!" she thought. "And Father gone across the river to the trading post!" Mother and Baby Johnny and she were all alone. Her heart thumped wildly.

She raced across the open pasture and ran like a frightened rabbit through the garden. There was their log cabin standing bravely in the clearing of the wild Ohio woods. She banged the cabin door behind her. She was safe.

"The windows, Janie! Help me, quick!" cried her mother.

Janie tugged at the heavy boards. As they dropped across the windows, she asked, "How many Indians did you see? Where did they come from?"

"The other side of the ridge, I think. There are only three. More than likely, they saw our chimney smoke. Don't be too frightened, Janie. Yesterday's rain wet the roof down, so they can't burn us out. We can stand them off well enough, even if the barrel of corn is almost empty. Your father'll get home any day now."

26

Mother tried to smile as she picked up a wooden bucket from the corner near the fireplace and went toward the back door.

"Mother, where are you going?" Janie cried.

"We need water," her mother said. "I'm going to the spring to fill the bucket. Bar the door after me, Janie. And if—if anything should happen, look after Johnny. Feed him if he cries, and fix him under his blanket nice and warm when night comes. Don't leave the cabin, Janie, no matter what happens. And remember, Father showed you how to load the musket. You know how to use it."

"Don't go. Please, Mother. They'll see you. Oh, it's all my fault about the water."

But Janie's cries were of no use. Her mother was gone. There was nothing for her to do but close the door and fasten it with the heavy wooden bar. Her hands shook, and tears ran down her face.

How happily she had run off to fish that morning without filling the water bucket! Father and Mother had warned her that the water bucket must always stand full, ready in case of need. She had forgotten because for over a year the Indians had left them alone.

Waiting

Johnny stirred suddenly in his cradle. He began to cry. He was so little and helpless and pink all over! His fuzzy yellow hair was soft and shiny. How Janie liked to hug him! She rocked the cradle and sang softly till he was quiet again.

Then Janie went over to a loophole in the wall and looked out. There was no sign of Mother, but she could see their vegetable garden full of yellow pumpkins and tall poles of frosted beans. It didn't seem as if there could be danger out there. A bright fire burned in the fireplace, but Janie felt cold all over.

28

She crossed the cabin now to look out on the side that faced the ridge of hills. She stood very still, with her eyes on the little apple trees near the cornfield two hundred yards away.

There they were—the Indians! She could see their hunting knives shining sharply in the sunlight. And Mother not back!

Janie ran across the room to look out again toward the spring. How was Mother going to get safely back without their seeing her? She couldn't run or bend over low with that heavy bucket of water. She would have to stand upright, even if the Indians did see her.

Here she came now. The sun made her hair shine with color like the frost-painted leaves. Even from here, her eyes looked as brown as an owl's feathers.

"How strange," Janie thought, "for me to think about things like that now, when I'm so frightened!" Her everyday, busy mother seemed different somehow—very wonderful and brave. If only she could get here before the Indians saw her!

There was a low whirring sound. An arrow whizzed through the garden. A wild whoop told Janie the Indians had seen her mother. She was hurrying now as fast as she could under the weight of the full bucket.

Whirrrr! Another arrow went whizzing through the air. The bucket fell to the earth as her mother ran for cover among the bean poles.

30

Janie gazed at a red spot that came out on the sleeve of her mother's dress, and watched her mother's face turn very white. Then she rushed to open the back door.

Her mother fell into a chair as Janie dropped the heavy wooden bar into place again. "Are you hurt badly, Mother?" she asked.

"My right arm, Janie," her mother said in a low voice. "You'll have to do the best you can to keep them off. Get the musket and load it, but don't fire until they come close."

Janie Does Her Part

Janie picked up the musket that always stood in the corner and reached for the powder horn. Her hands shook as she loaded the gun with powder and shot. It was too heavy for her to hold up. So she propped it over the tall chest of drawers, pushed it through the loophole facing the forest, and then watched and waited.

The whoops of the Indians woke Johnny in his cradle. He began to cry again. Arrow after arrow whizzed toward the cabin. Then there was a crash.

Janie turned around to see her mother's blue teapot broken to bits on the floor. One arrow had come through a mud-filled crack in the logs right into the dish cupboard.

That blue teapot and the tall chest were the only treasures left from her mother's home in Boston, where the streets were quiet and safe. There the ladies wore dainty dresses and pretty hats. Everyone went to church, and they had neighbors over for supper.

Janie's mother had told her stories about Boston over and over again. Some day, she always said, Janie would help make a place like that here in the Ohio woods. Then there would be schools and churches and friends and safety instead of wild Indians and lonely woods.

Whirrrrr! Whirrrrr! More arrows!

32

Janie looked out to see the Indians running toward the cabin, with their shiny hunting knives held high in their strong hands.

"Now, Daughter," her mother said.

Janie fired but she missed. Before she could reload the gun, the Indians with their shiny, sharp knives were on the roof, yelling and shrieking with joy.

So long as the fire roared in the great fireplace, they would not dare to drop down the chimney. But oh, if only Father were here!

Janie finished reloading the musket. The smell of gunpowder filled her nose and throat.

Then above Johnny's cries and the shrieking of the Indians, she heard a welcome voice.

The call came from way across the brook. "Hello! Mary! Janie! Johnny!" Janie saw their old brown horse come racing across the pasture. Father was riding low in the saddle and firing as he came. Close behind him rode three other men.

After that Janie was never just sure what did happen. The Indians' wild whoops stopped. Then Janie's arms were tight around her father's neck. And she was crying over and over, as if she were afraid it could not be so, "You're home, Father. You're home! You're home!"

"Yes, Janie," said Father, "just in time."

And one of the strangers with him said, "Those three Indians won't trouble you again. We finished two, and the third will fall in his tracks before he runs very far, I think."

Janie went over to her mother, and with her voice full of tears, she said, "I'll never, never forget to fill the bucket with water again. Never! Oh, Mother, I'm so sorry. It was my fault."

"You've found out the hard way, my little girl," her father said, "that it's wise to do as Father and Mother tell you."

34

A Real Thanksgiving Day

"It's all right, Janie," her mother said. She held her lips tight together while Father cut away her sleeve, washed the deep red cut in her arm, and tied a clean cloth around it.

"Try not to think any more about what might have happened," Father went on. "Do you know what day this is? Thanksgiving Day! I decided to get back in time to be with my family on Thanksgiving Day. Go look in my saddlebags, Janie. I bought a present for each of you."

Janie ran outdoors and came back with her arms full of packages. "Which one is for me, Father? Tell me, quick."

"Wait a minute, my dear, wait a minute!" Her father laughed. "The biggest package goes to your mother. Ten yards of cloth for a new dress, and a wooden doll for Johnny to help him cut his teeth!"

"And now, my chipmunk, see if you like what I picked out for you from the peddler's sack."

Janie was in such a hurry that her fingers were clumsy trying to untie the piece of deerskin around her package.

Then she began to dance in a giddy way, like a spinning top, calling out, "Shoes! Shoes! Look, Mother! Town shoes! My very first ones!"

She hugged the dainty blue slippers close.

"They're for special days only," her father said, his eyes sparkling. "For Sundays and singing school and—"

"For what, did you say?" her mother broke in.

"Singing school. We're going to have neighbors, Mary. These men who came home with me are going to help set up a town here, just as soon as logs can be cut for cabins. And then we shall have schools and churches and—"

Mother smiled at Janie and held her hand tight. "It's going to be the way I told you, Janie. And you can help make, here in Ohio, the kind of place Mother came from. Oh, this is a real Thanksgiving Day."

Katherine W. Eyre

The Starfish

Jerry's Tricks

Nine-year-old Peggy, with her eyes full of interest, watched her big brother Jerry. He was pulling a large starfish and a bunch of slippery seaweed out of the water.

"What are you going to do with that?" Peggy asked him.

"I'm going to hide it in Sven's bunk. Oh, boy, won't he be mad when he gets into bed tonight!" Jerry's blue eyes danced with fun at the thought.

Teasing Sven was the most fun eleven-year-old Jerry could think of. It was not that he didn't like Sven, but teasing the youngest logger was always the thing to do in a lumber camp. And Sven was the youngest logger.

Sven was so jolly that he nearly always just smiled at Jerry's teasing and jokes. But sometimes he would let out a howl and chase Jerry round and round and in and out among the loggers' houses and their tiny flower gardens. Then it was fun!

"You'll be sorry," Peggy warned her brother, as she tied her new blue scarf over her brown curls. "Dad's going to take me out in the big boat, and he won't take you."

But Jerry went right on with his plans. And while he was hiding the hard, rough starfish and wet seaweed in Sven's bunk, Sven was far up the woods road with the other loggers cutting down trees.

The next morning Jerry kept out of sight until the men had gone to work. He was a little bit afraid Sven really might not like this joke at all. Peggy, too, thought he might get mad this time. After all, a starfish!

That afternoon the children were fishing over the fence at one side of their float. Their camp was not built on land like most lumber camps. There was no flat land on which to build a camp. The hills, covered with trees, came right down to the seashore. So the houses and gardens of the loggers were on wooden floats.

Across the water came a sharp whistle, "Cheep, peep, pee-eep!" like a sea bird crying.

"The showboat," Peggy squealed as she looked out to sea.

"She's heading for Hanson's Landing!" Jerry let out a whoop. "They'll be showing movies there tonight. I'm going to ask Mother if we may go. You hold my line." He passed his pole to Peggy.

In a few minutes he came back whistling. "She says she thinks Dad is going to take the big boat, and a whole bunch of us will go. Isn't that great!"

Jerry was happy the rest of the afternoon, catching fish off the float and dabbling in the water. Once in a while he would dive in and swim about close to shore. Peggy lay on her bed reading, with the radio turned on.

"Jerry, Peggy! Supper," their mother called.

"Isn't Dad home yet?" Jerry asked as he sat down at the table.

"A big boom broke last night, and he's been out trying to pick up the drift logs," their mother told them in a worried voice. "He says it's kind of queer how many booms have been breaking lately. Too many logs are being lost. It looks as if someone was at work stealing logs."

Jerry and Peggy were so excited at the thought of going to the movies they could hardly eat their hot soup and crackers and strawberry shortcake. They washed the supper dishes, and still Dad hadn't come. Then they heard the sound of a motor warming up.

"That sounds like Sven's boat," Jerry said. "I guess he'll be taking a bunch to the movies."

"Run along and ask if there's room for you," Mother said.

40

Jerry went toward the door, but then he remembered the starfish. "I guess he's already got a full load without us," he said in a low voice. He was afraid to face Sven.

Peggy said nothing. She was thinking about the starfish, too, as she looked out of the doorway, hoping to see Dad's big boat. Instead, she saw a low dark boat with someone much too big sitting in the stern. It came slowly, hugging the shore.

"Here's Katie!" Peggy jumped from her chair. "Maybe I can swap my yellow scarf for a ride in her canoe."

Peggy ran out of the door with the yellow scarf flying from her hand. "Oh, Katie," she called to the large Indian woman, "will you take Mother and Jerry and me to Hanson's Landing to see the movies if I give you this?" Peggy swung the scarf back and forth.

"Yes," said Katie. "That's where I'm going."

The small motor in Katie's dugout canoe put-putted and then was still, as she brought the canoe alongside their landing and reached out for the pretty scarf.

"I'll wait here for Dad," Mother said, "but you children go. Only don't forget your sweaters."

Peggy ran back for the sweaters. Katie tied the yellow scarf around her black hair. Then she started the motor, and they were on their way.

Off to the Movies

They swung out around a rocky point and then headed into a long narrow bay. The lights of Hanson's Landing began to twinkle out against the dark forest. When they got to the landing, they found a trawler and all kinds of small boats lying against the wharf. But Katie found a place for her dugout and turned off the motor.

"How nice it feels to walk on a road!" Peggy said, as they left the wharf and their feet touched the ground. "We don't get the chance very often."

At a store they bought some candy and gum. Then they hurried to the wharf where the showboat was tied up.

42

Soon they were sitting inside the showboat, eating candy and waiting for the movie to begin. Sven was already there with some of the loggers. Jerry and Peggy stayed as far away from him as they could. They hoped the picture would begin before he saw them and remembered the starfish. Sven was laughing and talking with his friends and didn't even look their way.

The picture was exciting, and all too soon they saw THE END printed in large letters. That meant it was time to go home. They went out into the summer night and back to Katie's dugout.

As the canoe put-putted out of the bay, it left a trail of white light in the water. Peggy dabbled her hand and flung the shining drops here and there. "Pretty, isn't it?" she said.

43

A breeze had come up, and outside the bay
Katie had to head her little canoe into a fairly
hard wind. Every time the dugout dipped down
after a wave, water splashed over the bow, where
Jerry sat.

"You'd better bail, you two," Katie said from
the stern as she passed two cans forward. "I can
run for Kemp's Island and wait there till the
wind drops."

Jerry and Peggy dipped up water and flung it
out, but fast as they worked, the sea worked
faster. They were sitting in cold salt water, and
Peggy knew that her pretty pink dress would
never be the same.

"Better bail faster," Katie shouted above the
put-putting of the motor and the crash of the
waves. "It's not too rough, but the canoe's low in
the water. I'm afraid it'll get filled up."

Faster, faster, faster! They filled the cans with
the salty water and flung it over the side.

44

Slish, slosh! The water was moving back and forth in the bottom of the canoe as it rode up and down on the waves. Over their heads and down their necks went the cold water, as the waves came splashing high up and over.

"Katie would have been all right without us to weigh her down," Jerry was thinking to himself. "And Sven had lots of room in his boat. Why did I put that starfish in his bunk?"

Kemp's Island

At last the waves began to get smaller, and that meant they were near Kemp's Island. All of a sudden, bump! Jerry pitched forward, knocking Peggy against Katie's knees. Katie turned off the motor. "What's that?" she asked.

Jerry sat up and looked over the bow. "We ran into a drift log," he said. In the gleam of their lantern, he could see their own mark on the log.

"It must be one of the logs Dad is hunting for from the boom that broke last night." Jerry moved the canoe along the log, trying to find the other end.

45

"This log is fastened to another," he said.

"Look!" Peggy pointed into the darkness. "A light on Kemp's Island!"

"Cover our lights," Katie said.

She picked up a paddle and moved the canoe nearer to the shore. The island and the logs broke the strong wind. As they got closer to shore, they could hear the whine of a saw and the low voices of several men, who seemed to be working hard and fast in the darkness.

"They're sawing off our mark!" Jerry said in a low, excited voice.

"Stealing logs! We must get back to camp right away," Katie said. She pushed away from the shore, feeling her way along the logs. But she didn't turn on her motor or show her lights until she was sure of clear water ahead.

Then they went on again with the waves falling into the dugout as before. Faster and faster the children bailed, while their arms and backs grew terribly tired.

"I can't stand any more," Peggy said, almost crying.

"A light's coming," said Katie. "It looks like the big boat."

The sound of the strong motor grew louder. Jerry put his hands to his mouth and sent a shout through the darkness. A few minutes later Dad was helping them aboard the big boat. Then he tied the dugout behind.

"Rough going, isn't it?" was all he said.

"Dad, we found the men who are stealing logs. They're sawing our marks off now over on Kemp's Island."

"You don't say! So that's why the booms have been broken." Dad looked thoughtful for a minute. "I'll land you and then take some men to clean that crowd up. We'll take them by surprise this time of night."

When the tired children crawled from the boat to the landing float, Sven was waiting there, holding up a lantern to light them in. He looked as if he were really frightened and worried.

"You had it pretty rough," he said. "Why didn't you come in my boat?"

Jerry stood there all wet and looking foolish in the gleam of the lantern. "I was afraid you'd be mad at me about the starfish in your bunk."

"Starfish in my bunk? Did you put one there?" Sven suddenly roared with laughter. "Oh, ho! So that's why the cook gave me a mean look this morning! Cook slept in my bunk because I slept in the woods." He laughed again and shook his head with make-believe sadness. "Poor cook!"

Jerry felt foolish as he followed Peggy into the house. Their mother was waiting with towels and warm clothes and hot milk. Behind him he could still hear Sven's laughter. It was Sven who was enjoying the joke now!

But just the same, if it hadn't been for the starfish, they would never have gone in Katie's canoe. They would never have tried to find safety near Kemp's Island. They would never have found the men stealing the logs. So maybe the starfish idea hadn't been bad after all!

Helen Dickson

Becky and the Bandit

A Boy's Job

"Wake up, Becky! Wake up!"

Becky opened her eyes to see her mother bending over her bed with a tallow candle held high in one hand. Becky was very sleepy, but she smoothed her golden curls out of her eyes and tried to read her mother's face in the dancing light.

"Please, dear, try to understand me." Her mother's voice was worried.

The worry reached through into Becky's mind and made her wake up suddenly. She sat up, almost knocking the candlestick out of her mother's hand.

"What is it?" she asked, pushing her curls away from her face. "Isn't Papa any better this morning?"

"No," said her mother. "He can't go down the mountain after all. You'll have to go instead."

"Me?" cried Becky. Then, remembering that her sick father might be asleep, she said softly, "Am I to take the gold down for him?"

Mother set down the candle. "Yes, I want you to hurry now and dress for the ride. You must leave soon." Mother looked down at her small daughter for a minute.

Becky tumbled out of bed and jumped up and down as her feet hit the cold floor.

"This will be your chance to make believe you're a boy, Becky," said Mother. "You've always wished you were a boy. Now you must dress like one and act like one every step of the way. You will have to wear a pair of Simon's trousers and one of his shirts and put your hair up under Papa's cap."

Becky's eyes began to dance in the candlelight as she listened to the exciting plan. Holding her bright curls together all tight in one hand, she turned and smiled at herself in the looking glass. No one would ever be able to guess she was a girl if she had on trousers and a cap!

Becky and her family lived in the mountains east of the San Joaquin Valley many miles from town. Here her father had taken over a gold mine. With the help of his son, he had washed enough gold from the earth to keep his family and even to save a little money for later years.

Now it was time to take some gold down to the town to pay the tax on the mine. But he had caught a bad cold that had not got any better since last night. It would not be very wise for him to take the long, cold ride.

Simon, Becky's big brother, would have gone if he had been at home. But Simon had gone to try his luck at sea. He had left a few old clothes at home. Becky had often longed to try them on, but Mother had always said, "No, ladies do not wear men's clothes. You should try harder to be a lady."

Now Mother had changed her mind, for there was no one but Becky to make the hard trip down the mountain. Mother had to stay at home to take care of Father. But Becky wasn't afraid. The tax gold had to be paid and she would do it.

Adventure—Perhaps!

Then right in the middle of breakfast, Becky's heart jumped so wildly that she bit her tongue. She might even meet Joaquin Murrieta!

Joaquin Murrieta was a bandit who, with a bunch of bad men, traveled the roads of the San Joaquin Valley and the hills round about. He rode looking for whatever he might steal—a bag of gold in the pocket of some unlucky person, or a whole herd of cattle. Whatever Joaquin wanted, he took.

Just to speak his name was enough to make crying children stop their noise, and their mothers' faces grow white. Joaquin Murrieta was a real bandit, mean and heartless.

But sometimes he could be kind, too. Strange stories were told of his kindness to some unlucky people whose troubles touched his heart. But one could never be just sure how he might happen to be feeling. And his deeds were more often bad than kind. So people stayed as far away from him as they could. There were far more stories of his meanness than there were of his kindness.

52

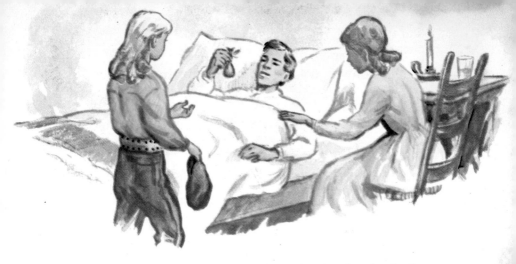

Now Becky stood at her father's bedside, listening to what she should do and how she should take the gold to the town tax office. But she had some trouble following his words. Her thoughts were still on the exciting chance of a meeting with the bandit.

At last her father handed her a little bag which she hung around her neck under Simon's blue shirt.

"Go straight to the tax office," he said. "If the taxes should go unpaid, someone would have the right to take our mine. And there are several people in the San Joaquin Valley who would like to have it. Take good care of the gold, Becky."

Becky promised herself that no one would ever get it from her, not even Joaquin Murrieta!

53

The dawn was beginning to show above the eastern hills when Becky swung into her saddle. She waved good-by to Mother, then spoke to Prince. The horse stepped forward, and Becky was on her way.

It was fun to be riding like a boy instead of sideways as a lady should. Never in all her ten years had she felt so much like a boy. With her curls pushed up under the cap, her head felt free. Every inch of her felt ready for anything, and for one daring minute she almost hoped she would meet Joaquin Murrieta.

The sun was up and the world awake by the time Becky reached the banks of Bear Creek. The first danger of her journey was at hand. The creek was wider than Becky had ever seen it, and she knew at one look that the middle of it would be well over Prince's back. That meant that the horse would have to swim. Where would be the safest crossing? She did not know.

And then it came to her that Prince should know where it would be best to cross the creek. She would give him his head and let him choose his own way. Quietly she told him to go forward.

54

He walked carefully down the bank and into the water. Down, down he went, and the water came up. It was above his knees now, higher and higher. The icy water covered Becky's feet, then her knees.

All at once she knew Prince was swimming. His head was stretched out flat before him, and she could feel his feet working under him. She could see the other bank of the creek coming closer.

At last she felt a bump, and then Prince began climbing up the bank. They were safely across! Becky, shivering with cold, felt for the heavy lump under the blue shirt. The bag of gold was there, quite safe.

The sun was high, Becky and Prince had both dried from their swim, and they had almost reached the valley floor when, rounding a hill, they met the bandit.

Bandit's Gold

The minute Becky saw the bunch of horsemen all wearing guns, she knew it was Joaquin Murrieta and his men. It was easy to pick out the leader. He sat on his horse and watched her with a slow, heartless smile, while every bit of color went out of Becky's face.

At last, "Good day," said the bandit.

Becky swallowed and said nothing. Instead she galloped forward, hoping against hope that the men would part and let her ride on her way. But when she came up to the leader, he put his horse across Prince's path, stopping him.

"Not so fast," he said smoothly. "You are a long way from home, my fine boy. Yes?"

Still Becky said nothing. Her fear was quieted for a minute because the bandit thought she was a boy.

"And what are you doing so far from home? It is now the time for taking tax money to town. No?" The bandit was watching her.

Still Becky held her tongue, while her heart beat wildly.

56

"It is a little queer for a boy to be traveling these lonely roads without a good reason. I think I know your reason." His voice became suddenly hard, and his black eyes grew small and mean. "Hand over your gold."

Then at last Becky spoke. Lifting the bridle, she shouted, "Hi," and banged her feet sharply into Prince's sides.

The horse jumped forward so suddenly that he almost got through the bunch of surprised men. Almost! Then the men closed in around him, and Becky couldn't get away.

One of the men tried to pull her from the saddle. But Becky had decided to fight. They must not get Father's gold. Strongly she hit out at the dark smiling face before her. The man fell back, but another rushed his horse to her side.

In the fight which followed, Father's old cap was brushed from Becky's head, and her curls came loose. They fell to her shoulders, shining like gold. Becky was more frightened than ever. Now they would see that she was a girl and helpless against them. How could a girl stand off these mean men? They would laugh at her trying to fight them!

Then suddenly, above the noise of the horses' feet and her frightened cries, Becky heard a voice shouting, "Stop! Stop! Let her go."

The crowd fell back to let Joaquin Murrieta ride up to where Becky sat on Prince, with her golden hair bright about her shoulders.

"So you are a girl," he said, and his voice was gentle and full of surprise. It was almost kind.

For a minute Becky and the bandit eyed one another. Then the man smiled a slow smile. "So. It is just as I thought. You did have gold with you after all." He was looking at her shining hair. "Never have I seen gold so beautiful, and I must have it."

"Oh, my," thought Becky, shivering with fear, "is he going to cut off all my hair?"

58

All at once her curls, which she had always disliked, seemed very, very wonderful to her.

As she watched with frightened eyes, Murrieta drew a hunting knife from his belt. Moving his horse close alongside Prince, he reached for one of Becky's curls.

His men watched with interest, but not one said a word as their leader's knife cut through one curl and he held it up for all to see. With a low bow over his saddle horn to Becky, he put the prize into his shirt pocket.

"I wish only one curl, *Señorita*," he said as he put his knife back into his belt. "I will not be heartless and take all your gold from you. Murrieta is not the enemy of little girls. Thank you." He signaled to his men and they drew their horses back. "Go now. *Adiós*."

Becky didn't wait for Murrieta to have a change of heart. With a touch of the bridle, she sent Prince down the road in a wild gallop. Father's gold was safe.

Late that day, Becky reached the town without having to go through any more adventures. She walked into the tax office and handed over the little bag of gold. She was given a piece of paper that said the taxes for the mine were paid. Becky put the piece of paper in her pocket.

The mine was safe, thanks to Becky's golden curls.

Many years later, when Becky had become an old lady with eyeglasses on her nose and all her golden curls were sparkling white, she liked to tell her grandchildren about her meeting with the bandit.

"So you see," she used to say, eyeing her granddaughters over the tops of her glasses, "it is wisest for girls to be happy always that they are girls."

But her granddaughters didn't always look as if they thought so!

Doris Gates

John Hudson's Surprise

The Secret Plan

"Boy!"

"Yes, sir?"

John Hudson stood on the ship's deck before the captain and tried to look him straight in the eye. It was not easy because John had done something he shouldn't. And the captain always saw through everyone.

"You left the ship yesterday," said the captain, "without asking leave." Captain Henry Hudson believed in coming right to the point even with his own son.

The boy swallowed. "Yes, sir. I did."

As the big man looked hard at the boy, the wide eyes in his gruff face became a little softer. Who would not be proud of a boy who stood and faced what he had done?

Captain Hudson was thoughtful for a minute. Then he said, "You know that I told the crew they must not leave the ship, don't you? It is for the crew's own good."

"Yes, sir," answered John.

For several minutes there was quiet. "Why did you go, boy?" asked the captain at last. "Don't you know that I have enough troubles without some more because of you?"

John nodded his head. How well he knew! He was only the cabin boy, but he had eyes and ears. He knew that the crew disliked his father and had talked against him almost from the very day they had sailed from home.

Their ship, the good *Half Moon*, had sailed ever to the north in the hope of discovering the northern way to India. Huge pieces of ice had almost broken the tiny ship, but his father had got them safely away. And now they had come to this more southern point, still hoping to discover the waterway to India. But it had turned out to be only a very wide river.

Yes, John knew about the troubles Captain Henry Hudson was having.

62

He nodded his head sadly. "I did not mean to make trouble, sir."

"Then what did you mean to do?"

The boy was quiet. He dared not answer. His father would think his adventure foolish. John himself began to wonder if, after all, maybe it was foolish. It had seemed such a wonderful idea in the beginning!

"I cannot say, sir."

Then Captain Hudson spoke almost angrily. "You must know what a chance you take when you leave the ship. These Indians are all right as long as we keep them in their place and have the ship between us. But for a boy to row ashore and go off into the woods alone is too daring."

It was not so much that he was angry about the boy's adventures as that he was upset because John had been in danger.

But John said nothing. He just waited.

"You must learn to keep the rules," decided the captain. "It doesn't matter that you are my son. You must be taught to do as you are told."

"Yes, sir."

Captain Hudson thought about it for a while. His eyes looked across the sparkling bay in which they were anchored, and followed the line of the forest along the shore. All the trees had turned a bright red, and the water below them shone with the same color. No wonder the boy wanted to get into the woods. But he must be taught to keep the rules.

Captain Hudson spoke gruffly. "Go to the cook. You are to stay under him, cleaning fish and washing pots until we lift anchor. You understand?"

"Yes—yes, sir," answered John.

His father knew that he could not have picked on anything that the boy more disliked to do. He took it like a man, however, and turned to go.

"And, boy!" said Captain Hudson.

"Yes, sir?"

"Try not to be so much like me. It will keep you out of much danger."

64

John smiled. Then he went slowly to the cook, who was glad enough to have a little help. The cook set him at once to the cleaning of a huge fish which they were to have at noon.

John cleaned away with a will, but his thoughts were going round and round. He must think and plan, think and plan. Yesterday he had made a start on the plan. Today he must finish it.

What his father did not know was that he had not only seen Indians the day before, but had also talked with them about something special.

They were boys no older than he, but they had something which John knew every one of the crew, even the captain himself, would give almost anything to have. And John meant to get it for them, for it was very important. It might mean the difference between a happy crew on the way home or a very unhappy one.

But how was he to get away? He thought about this all morning. He had to go to the Indians again. They were too afraid to come to him. He had no way of knowing they would keep their promise, but he must try to keep his.

The only thing he could think to do was to wait until dusk. Then he would make believe he was weary from the day's work, and go to the stern deck for a little sleep.

The cook and the crew would laugh at him, but if luck were with him, everyone except the watchman would stay below decks talking. Then if he moved quietly, he could keep his promise to meet the Indian boys in the woods.

He thought it would never, never get dark. But at last dusk fell, and John went about carrying out his plan.

A Good Trade

When his boat reached the shore of the bay, John was all out of breath from rowing hard, but just the same he raced for the meeting place.

Suppose the Indian boys hadn't waited for him! He stopped by the big spring. No one was in sight.

His heart fell. He began to wish he had not come. It was so dark in the thick woods!

Then he could see the Indian boys slowly coming toward him out of the darkness.

As the Indians reached him, they began to talk by making signs with their hands.

Using signs is a very slow way to talk, and the Indians grew excited. Again and again, John had to tell himself to take his time, for he was not going to let the boys get the better of him.

In the end he was successful. They had to give in. That made him feel very grown up.

The Indians even helped to carry the heavy baskets down to the water's edge and load them into the boat before he gave them his buttons. Then waving and shouting as though much pleased with themselves, they watched him row away.

John went swiftly toward the *Half Moon*, where he could see torches lighted on deck. Something must have happened while he was gone. He used all his might to row faster, till he was close to the great anchor cable.

"Is that you, boy?" a voice called sharply from the deck.

"Y-yes, sir," John answered.

He could see his father now, near the rail, shouting down to him, "Where have you been?"

John answered quickly. He was beginning to be afraid his adventure was not going to end so successfully as he had hoped.

"What is it you have there?" asked the captain.

"Chestnuts," said John.

"Chestnuts!" cried out Captain Hudson.

"Chestnuts!" shouted the men as they gathered to watch. "Chestnuts! Enough for us all?" they asked.

"Enough," said John, "and more. Twelve whole baskets full."

"Twelve!" said the captain. "How did you come by them?"

It was as though John had said he had a boatload of gold. The men could not have been more pleased. They were weary of living on hard bread and fish and wild game. Chestnuts would mean a jolly feast to them. Even though they had had some of the sweet nuts up the river, it had not been enough. And now this boy had twelve whole baskets full!

"I traded them for my buttons," said John. "Two baskets for a button."

John thought his father would surely put him in irons and keep him there the rest of the trip. It was very quiet on deck as the men waited for Henry Hudson to speak.

At last he said, "It strikes me that we are both of us, boy, always wanting to do things full of danger. The only difference is that the things I do don't turn out so well as yours." Then he laughed.

Suddenly the unhappy feeling of the men changed. They said that even though Henry Hudson had not had success in finding the north waterway to India, he had found something. He had discovered this river where chestnuts grew. They even seemed proud of their captain now.

"John," said Captain Hudson.

"Yes, sir," said John, and he looked up at his father in the torch light. He was greatly surprised that his father should speak to him by name. Until now he had always been just "boy."

"Come up, John, and join me in the cabin."

As John followed his father to the cabin, he knew he was no longer a boy. He was John. He was John Hudson, a man, with a man's work behind him. And the crew were feeling jolly. They would not be finding fault with everything during the long trip home.

Mosser Mauger

Neighbors Round the World

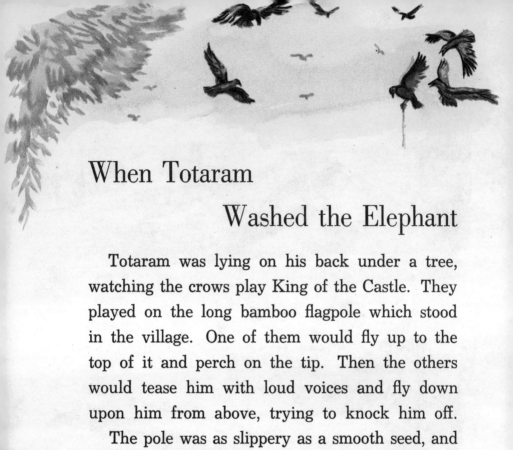

When Totaram
Washed the Elephant

Totaram was lying on his back under a tree, watching the crows play King of the Castle. They played on the long bamboo flagpole which stood in the village. One of them would fly up to the top of it and perch on the tip. Then the others would tease him with loud voices and fly down upon him from above, trying to knock him off.

The pole was as slippery as a smooth seed, and no crow could stay king for long. But what fun he had during that time! He would flap his wings and tell them all what a fine crow he was, and then—! Down came another crow on top of him and sent him flapping into the air.

As Totaram lay watching this game, suddenly he heard a sound behind him and jumped as a sleeping dog does before a cart wheel touches it.

"Have you nothing better to do than watch the crows and sleep like a bat in the daytime?" asked the man beside him.

Totaram made a deep bow, bending low from the waist, because the man was the keeper of the elephants and an important person.

"What is your mother doing?" asked the man.

"She is working in the fields," said Totaram.

"And your father?"

"He has gone to the jungle to cut bushes to put around his fields to keep out the wild pigs."

"And your sister Jai?"

"She is making something for our supper," said Totaram, who was beginning to feel very uncomfortable.

"And you?"

"I am doing nothing at all," said Totaram slowly. "But truly I would do something if I could find it to do."

"Why are you not with the other boys watching the cows?"

Totaram hung his head like wheat when the grains are ripe and heavy upon it.

"Because, O Great One," he said, "I teased one of the cows with my pointed stick. And she ran into the village and upset four bowls of milk as she ran. How could I know that she would mind the stick so much? And the milkman beat me and sent me away."

"Little Trouble Maker," said the man, "I will give you another chance. But there must be no more foolishness or teasing. You must not act like one of the monkeys in the jungle."

Totaram lifted his head.

"I want a boy to wash the big elephant," the keeper went on. "Every Wednesday and every Saturday I will take her to the pool near the gate of the city. You must meet me there when the sun is in the middle of the sky. Take with you some coconut shells to scrub with."

Totaram could hardly believe his good luck and ran off to tell the boys about it. The keeper of the elephants looked at the crow on top of the pole, and then he looked at the boys who were waving their arms about and talking.

"They are much alike, boys and crows," the keeper said smiling, and went away.

Totaram thought that Wednesday would never come. He teased the gray kitten, pulling its tail until it mewed and his sister Jai cried.

His mother sighed and said, "Little Trouble Maker, use your strong arms at this," and gave him the heavy stick to pound the brown rice.

At last Wednesday came, and when the sun was high, and the pigeons were talking softly in the trees, Totaram set out for the pool. He arrived before the elephant and sat down under a wild fig tree to wait.

Then came the elephant, like a black mountain, toward him. Totaram felt the size of a rabbit, and then he felt the size of a mouse. Then he thought, "If it comes much nearer, I shall be as nothing at all!"

The keeper laughed at him. "Are you a squirrel come to wash my elephant?" he asked. "You looked larger in your village. I could use twenty of you little ones."

Totaram's knees shook as the dry grass does in the swift winds of the hot season.

But Totaram held on to his coconut shells
hard and followed the keeper down to the water.
There the enormous elephant gave a sigh of
happiness and lay down on her side. And
Totaram climbed on top of her and began to
scrub her with his coconut shells.

It was long work. "Surely I am cleaning a
mile of elephant," he said to himself, and looked
hopefully to see if the keeper would say that his
work was finished. But the man was smoking a
water pipe under the fig tree and was lost in
thought.

Totaram had long since forgotten to be afraid, and he even dared to scrub in the elephant's big ears and around her little eyes.

That evening when he went home he had money in his pocket, and he was so proud that he called all his friends together to tell them what a wonderful boy he was. And he pulled the gray kitten's tail again.

When Saturday came, Jai and two village boys followed Totaram into the city and to the pool. The keeper lay down and went to sleep under the wild fig tree. And Totaram began scrubbing behind the elephant's ears as though he had been cleaning elephant's ears all his life.

"O my grandfathers!" said one boy. "Her right ear is as large as my father's dinner plate."

"Her left ear is the size of my uncle's umbrella," said the other boy. "Aren't you afraid, Totaram?"

"Oh my, no," said Totaram. "The elephant may be enormous, with ears like umbrellas, but she is as stupid as a mountain."

He began to jump up and down on her back to show them how brave he was.

The elephant moved one ear slowly, like a banana leaf in the wind. Totaram went on jumping. The elephant moved the other ear slowly, like a sail in a fishing boat. Totaram went on jumping.

Suddenly the elephant reached up her trunk, took Totaram around the waist and ducked him in the muddy water. Then she lifted him up and shook him the way a cat does a mouse. Then she ducked him again. Jai and the two boys laughed until they tumbled down and rolled over and over.

78

"She is as stupid as a mountain, is she?" called one boy.

"Now you know how my gray kitten feels when you pull its tail," said Jai.

"O queen of elephants," cried Totaram, "set me down, and I will never pull the gray kitten's tail again."

The elephant shook him again.

"O wisest of elephants," said Totaram, "truly I will never jump on you again."

Then the elephant set him down, and he ran away into the jungle near the village, where he could not see Jai and the two boys, who were still laughing.

Late that afternoon his mother found him there with his head on a gray root, fast asleep. He was saying something, and when she leaned over him, she heard, "I will never pull the gray kitten's tail again."

Irene Mott Bose

Auno and Tauno

Off to School

It is winter in Finland. For three long months, lights will be burning in all the little wooden houses from one end of the land to the other. They burn mostly in the daytime, for the days are gray like kittens' fur.

But at night the great white moon and the stars light up the snow. They throw a soft half-light, as if some good fairy had come flying low to brush the earth with her shining wings.

Sometimes bright-colored Northern Lights shine across the night sky.

Winter or summer, whatever the season, the family awakens early. Papa claps his hands, and the twins in two little homemade beds stretch and open their eyes.

Mama is busy between the oven and the table. Little curls of steam are coming from the copper coffeepot. Auno and Tauno can watch all that Mama does as they dress, for the house has one great room. It is the kitchen, living room, and bedroom.

Auno and Tauno always have two breakfasts: first a quick breakfast of coffee and dark bread, and then a real breakfast. After the quick breakfast they hurry out to play in the gray light until the real breakfast time.

No child of Finland has to be called more than once to come in for the real breakfast. What a big breakfast it is! Steaming potatoes and different kinds of fish, and other things too! And with Jack Frost and the north wind at work over the country night and day, the children are always ready to eat.

R8

After breakfast Auno and Tauno put on their skis and call, "Good-by, Mama! Good-by, Papa!"

They are dressed in heavy clothes, mufflers, and two pairs of wool stockings. The only way Mama and Papa can tell Auno from Tauno is by her yellow pigtails.

Inside the bags tied over their shoulders, they carry fish and sandwiches, and books too. And in Auno's bag there is a stiff, white apron.

Outside, the air is clear and still. The snow is so deep that it covers all but the tops of the fences. Auno and Tauno glide over the rolling country, their skis making fairy music over the hard top snow. Up and down the hills they go, as if they were on a roller coaster.

A deer, frightened by their laughter, runs back into the forest. Foxes rush into holes under the snow-covered stones. White rabbits jump across the snow like little puffs of wind.

Now the twins are coasting along a path between two lakes. Ahead they see the white flag of Finland against a gray sky. It waves over their red schoolhouse.

A good many pairs of skis are already leaning against the side of the building. Auno and Tauno put theirs at the end of the line. Then they brush the snow from their boots with little birch twigs that are tied together.

What a noise inside as good mornings are called! Frosty mittens are put into pockets, and cold fingers are clapped against bright red faces.

Auno puts on her stiff, white apron and takes one of the double seats. And Tauno, because he is full of fun, has to sit beside a very quiet little girl in another double seat.

With all the little girls wearing stiff, white aprons, the room looks as if white butterflies had settled there. But pretty Miss Maki is not looking at the aprons. She looks at hands, neck, and ears. Any boy or girl who is not as clean as a copper kettle is quickly sent home to wash. Auno and Tauno always breathe a little easier after she has finished.

Trouble for Tauno

While school is good enough, Auno and Tauno are always glad for the noon time. Then the boys play games, and the girls learn how to cook.

One game the boys play is like baseball, except that a stick of wood is used for a ball. When the batter hits the wood a good hard blow and sends it into the air, he must shout, "Get out below!"

Today, in the excitement of the game, Tauno forgot to call, "Get out below." And the flying stick whizzed through the air, taking a boy's cap right off his head.

Miss Maki happened to be looking out of the window at that very time. Knocking · on the window, she called Tauno in. She was very angry. Her eyes blazed like the Northern Lights.

"Tauno!" she scolded. "You might have killed your schoolmate. Boys who forget the rules must stand behind the blackboard and stay after school."

At three o'clock Tauno had to take his place behind the blackboard. The other children could see nothing of him but his new boots.

84

The wall clock ticked on and on. Auno felt so sorry for Tauno that every now and then a big tear would roll down her face and drop on to her book.

But behind the blackboard queer things were going on!

At first Tauno did nothing. Then one foot went to sleep. He felt as if hundreds of needles were dancing up and down his leg. He stood on the other foot. If only he could step out of his boots and jump around in his stockings!

Suddenly an idea came to Tauno. Why not step out of his boots? Yes, why not? Even the ticking clock seemed to say, "Why not?"

Ever so quietly Tauno pulled one foot out and then the other, and tiptoed to the coatroom door. No one had seen him. His boots still stood behind the blackboard as if he were in them!

When Auno reached home, her eyes stuck out like marbles, for there was Tauno, sitting on the brick warming oven. He was as happy as could be. She looked at his feet. His stockings were full of holes.

"Why, Tauno," she cried, "how—your boots—"

Tauno laughed until the tears rolled down his face. "Won't Miss Maki get a surprise when she tells my boots they can go home?"

"But what did Mama say?"

"Mama isn't home," he answered. Then he clapped his hands over his mouth. "There she comes, Auno. What shall I tell her about my new boots?"

Auno hurried to the window. Sure enough! It was Mama all right.

"Wear your old ones."

"I can't. Mama gave them away," said Tauno.

Quickly Auno ran to get a pair of her own boots. "Here, Tauno! They're old and stiff, but they will cover your feet."

Both Auno and Tauno pulled and tugged, and somehow Tauno's feet were squeezed into the small boots just as Mama walked into the house.

"Hello, children. Why, Auno! You're still wearing your school apron. Get into your play clothes, both of you." Mama didn't even look at Tauno's feet. She was very busy.

After school it is Noisy Time in Finland. That is the time for skiing and the high jump and all kinds of games. Children's shouts echo through the forests. Any child who does not want to play at Noisy Time is quickly taken to see the doctor.

"Why don't you go to meet your schoolmates near the lake?" asked Mama.

"Oh, good!" cried Auno, hurrying into her play clothes.

"I guess I'll study," said Tauno.

Mama looked frightened. She felt Tauno's head. "Go find Papa at once."

Tauno tried not to limp as he went after Papa.

"Tauno is not well," Mama told Papa. "He must take a steam bath today. Then tomorrow we will see the doctor."

So Papa built a blazing fire in the little log bathhouse, and when the stones were red hot, he called Tauno.

Tauno had a bad time getting the boots off. When they came off at last, he wiggled his toes to see if they were still on.

Papa had just poured cold water on the hot stones, and it made a funny sound as it turned into steam.

There were benches around the walls, just like those at the circus. Papa climbed to the top bench because the hotter it was, the better he liked it. Tauno took the lowest bench.

"How good this feels!" he thought to himself, as little drops of sweat came out on his shoulders and rolled down his back.

Soon Papa came down and threw more water on the stones for more steam. Next he switched Tauno lightly all over with green twigs. This switching did not hurt. It just made Tauno feel good and hot. After that they both covered themselves with soap and threw water at each other. Then they ran out of the bathhouse to roll over and over in the snow before they dressed.

The next morning Tauno thought he should tell Mama everything. But he had waited so long that it seemed harder than ever now. Oh, if only he had told her yesterday!

Once more he squeezed his feet into Auno's boots and tried not to limp. He could hear the jingle of little bells, and he knew that Papa had fed the white horse and was getting it ready for the long drive into town.

Off to the Doctor

"Ready!" cried Papa, and out of the house came Mama and Auno and Tauno. They all climbed into the sleigh and put their feet under the hay. Then Papa put a great deerskin around the twins' shoulders. Auno and Tauno looked like turtles, with only their heads sticking out.

How warm and cozy they were, while white snowflakes fell like stars on the white horse's back! The snow-covered trees were bent like trolls with long white whiskers. The bells on the horse jingled as the sleigh swept across the ice-covered lake.

Men were cutting holes in the ice, planting a line of cut evergreen trees to show travelers the way across the lake.

90

As soon as they reached town, the horse was tied up, and the family walked along the stone streets to the doctor's office.

"Well, well," said the doctor. "If it isn't some friends of mine! How is Auno? And Tauno?"

"He is not himself today, Doctor. He would not play in Noisy Time yesterday. He wanted to study. And when he thinks I am not looking," said Mama, "he looks as if something hurts."

The doctor looked at Tauno's eyes and tongue and throat. He felt to see if Tauno's heart was all right, and if he were too hot. At last he told him to run up and down the room five times. Tauno ran as best he could, trying not to limp.

"Well," said the doctor in a quiet voice. "Well-ll, I think it's his feet."

"His feet!" cried Papa and Mama.

"Yes, his feet. The boots are much too tight. Why, feel his toes. They are all curled up."

"Tauno," said Mama, looking closely, "are those your boots?"

And then both children had to tell everything, and there was great excitement until the doctor held up his hands for quiet.

Because he had been bad, Tauno had to remain in the sleigh while the family saw all the fun of market day. But his feet hurt so much that he was glad to curl up cozily in the hay and sleep while snowflakes drifted slowly down.

At noon he fed the white horse some of the warm hay at his feet. Just then the family came back with sandwiches and coffee. And soon they were headed for home.

Auno gave Tauno a punch. Papa was taking the turn to the schoolhouse. Tauno thought he was in for it now. The good old horse walked slowly as if he knew what was ahead for Tauno.

Tauno hoped that Miss Maki had gone home, but there was a light in the schoolhouse. "Oh, dear!" thought Tauno.

Papa entered the schoolhouse, and everyone followed. Miss Maki looked up in surprise.

"Good day," began Papa. "Tauno has something to say to you."

Now it was Tauno's turn to look surprised. He looked at Auno and Mama and Papa. No one helped him. Suddenly his eyes found his boots that he had left behind the blackboard.

92

"Oh, please, Miss Maki, may I put on my boots and finish my standing?"

Miss Maki smiled. "Put your boots on, Tauno," she said kindly, "but from the way you walk, I don't think you need to stand any more."

Soon the sleigh swept over the snow as if it were headed right for the Northern Lights.

Tauno was sure nothing in the world could be more beautiful. He felt all comfortable inside, even if his feet were still hurting. How glad he was to have Mama and Papa know everything, and how good they were not to scold him! He gave a little pull to Auno's pigtail, and they both laughed merrily into the silver stillness like the tinkling music from the bells.

Marguerite Henry

Way Ping, Master of Boats

A Boat with Eyes

"Stand away, stand away, Son," called Father to the boy who stood on the narrow deck and looked off to the west. "It is time to drop the anchor, so our boat may rest for the night. Stand away, my Son."

Way Ping had just been thinking that this boat was the nicest home in the world in the summer time. He was so glad he and Father and Mother and the new Sister lived on it. He had to work hard and help Father. But all the time he worked he could hear the brown waves slap the nose of the boat, and he could see the sunshine run over the deck like gold water.

94

It was evening now. Way Ping had forgotten how long he had stood watching the sunset. It seemed as if his heart had gone away to talk to the clouds and to follow the birds that went flying to their homes in the south. So when Father called to him, Way Ping jumped quickly, and his heart came running back to him.

He said, "Yes, Father, I hear, and tonight I shall not let a brown wave come up and slap me. Did you see that wave last night, Father? It acted as if it wanted to push me down and jump on me. But when I ran away and laughed, it only threw some spray in my face and went back again. Aren't waves funny, Father? There, the anchor is down in the mud now, isn't it? I know the sound when it hits the bottom of the river."

The boat pulled a little at the anchor chain. Then it drifted around until its stern rested near the reeds on the bank.

When the boat was still, Father put a board from the deck to the land, took a big market basket, and went off on shore to buy food for supper. Father always bought the food in the little villages that were near the river's edge.

He turned as he went off and called to Way Ping, "I'm going, Son. Remember, remember well, while I am gone, you are the Master of the Boat. Watch that nothing happens to it. Take care of the Mother and Sister and tighten the anchor chain if the boat rocks loose."

Of course Way Ping was very proud to be told this. Father always made him the Master of the Boat when he was gone, and Way Ping was very careful. He liked the boat so much.

It was such a pretty boat! The bottom of it was quite flat, but the two ends reached high into the air like the points of a new gold moon. The wood of the boat was gold-colored, too, and rubbed bright with Chinese oil. There were two masts and two square sails made of yellow cloth.

Way Ping went up to see if the sails were tight for the night. He tried the ropes and tied them well at the ends. There was one very big square sail and one little one. Sometimes only the big sail was up. That was when the wind was blowing high and puffed the yellow sail out very full. Then the little sail lay down near the deck, floppy and tired.

96

Way Ping was always sorry for the second sail when it could not stand up and push the wind and shine in the sun. So tonight he gave the little sail a soft pat as he tied it tightly. He said to it, "Never mind because you have to lie still now. It's night time and you must get rested for tomorrow. I think tomorrow you will stand up against the wind."

Then Way Ping had to go to the front of the boat to see if the little lamp that remained there all night was burning. He knew for sure that Father had lighted it, but since he was Master now, maybe he ought to see if it was quite all right.

On the front of the boat were painted two big, round, red eyes. They were the eyes of the ship. They did not look like eyes, but Way Ping knew they were, for Father had said, "Those, Son, are the eyes of our boat. They never go to sleep. They watch all day and all night to keep us safe. The boat's eyes see through the fog. You must be careful, Son, never to make the boat angry at us so it would shut its eyes."

All the time Way Ping had lived on the boat he had been careful. Now he looked to see if the lamp was burning brightly. In the light he could see the eyes, and he thought they were very friendly. He liked the ship's eyes. They had always been good to him and Mother and Father.

Even the new Sister had been held up to see the eyes. She liked the bright red color of them, and she made funny noises, trying to talk to them.

The Master at Work

The next thing Way Ping did was to see if the
ship's freight was all right. The big jars of bean
oil were piled high in the back. Way Ping thought
they looked quite safe. They were important,
for it was because of this oil that Way Ping's
father had to take his boat on the long journey.

You see, in China there are not many trains,
and few motor trucks, and not very many good
roads. To the Chinese people, the river is a wide
road, the Road of Boats. And when a man wants
to send freight from one city to another, he often
gets a boat to carry it for him.

Way Ping's father was a boatman. He had
filled his boat with this load of bean oil, and
was taking it two hundred miles up the river to
a store in a great city. All day long he sailed the
boat up the brown river. And if there was a
moon for light and the wind had not gone away,
sometimes the boat would sail all night, too.

But most nights the boat was anchored by the
shore, and Father would walk off the boat to the
land as he had tonight.

Always while Father was gone, Way Ping was Master of the Boat and very, very proud.

The most exciting place in the boat, except right by the big sail when the wind blew hard, was the room down under the deck. There Way Ping slept, and there Mother made the tea and took care of the Sister. It was a low, dark room. To go down to it, Way Ping pulled a ring in a board, the board came up like a door, and there were little steep wooden steps to climb down.

Mother and Sister were down in the room now. Way Ping thought he would call down to see if they were all right, before he went to fix the anchor for the night.

So he pulled the ring, opened the little door, and called down, "Oh, Mother, you there? You all right? Where is the little Sister? Father hasn't come back with the supper yet, but he'll be home soon, I think."

Mother's voice called back, "Yes, Son, I tend the fire of reed grass back here, and the little Sister is safe asleep in her corner. Are the sails fast? Take care that the anchor does not slip. Be careful, Big Son."

100

Way Ping started off to see about the anchor, but just at that minute he heard a little cry down the stairs. "Oh," thought he, "May-May is awake and crying. Mother is busy, so I had better go down and put her to sleep again."

Very, very quietly he climbed down the steep stairs and walked across the half-dark room to the corner where little Sister was lying. She didn't have any bed. She just had two big blue quilts put round and round her, and she lay quite happy on the floor most of the time. The rocking of the boat helped her to sleep, and the sound of the reeds swishing against the boat was her lullaby.

But now she was hungry, for she had slept a long time. So she cried and kicked till she had almost unrolled from the quilts. Way Ping rolled her up again gently.

"Such kickings!" he said. "You ought to be a boy, May-May. Then when you grow up, you could be a big, strong boatman. Don't cry. I'll turn you west now. Did you dream all the east dreams about the sun coming up like a great gold fish and getting caught in the clouds?"

Of course, May-May did not understand Way Ping, but she knew his voice, and it was nice to be turned to the west. Way Ping patted her softly, softly, and sang the lullaby his mother used to sing to him when he was a baby:

Mother of Dreams,
This little child cries
For the west dreams now.
Long has she slept with her face to the east,
Now she is turned to the west—
Mother of Dreams, Mother of Dreams,
Send her the west dreams now.

Hush, Baby, hush.
Dreams of the sunset, dreams of the dusk,
Dreams of the birds going home.
West dreams, rest dreams
From the Mother of Dreams to you.

102

A Bad Surprise

It seemed as if the boat helped to put May-May to sleep. It rocked back and forth among the swishing grasses. Way Ping wondered if the anchor chain was holding. As soon as May-May slept, he ran up to see about the anchor.

It seemed, as he went up the stairs, that the boat moved in a strange way, and when he got on deck he could not see the lights of the village. He ran around the deck. Then he saw that his boat was really moving, going away from the shore. Its anchor was loose and dragging.

At first he was too frightened to move. What would Father say? How could he ever get back to the village to find Father? Oh, why had he not tightened the anchor chain first of all? He wanted to cry. Then, like a real voice, he seemed to hear Father say, "You are the Master of the Boat, Son." So he had to be brave.

"I'll call Mother," he said. "We've got to get the boat steered around and the big sail put up." So he ran to the back and called Mother. She left her fire and came quickly.

"Don't be afraid, Son," she said. "We are two, and you are strong. We will get back to land again."

Way Ping had never worked so hard. He pulled in the anchor that had been dragging along in the mud, and he and Mother got the big sail up, and he steered the boat.

He and Mother talked to the boat as they worked. They begged it not to shut its eyes. They said to the eyes, "Help us, eyes of the boat. Watch in the dark for us. We can see so little, and we are not very good at this work."

Way Ping felt as if the boat really heard and helped them, for suddenly out of the dusk came Father's voice, and there they were, nearly to the shore again.

Father said, "Here I am, here I am, Son of mine. Steer west, more west. There, drop the sail." And then Father jumped on the boat from the land and fastened the anchor quite tightly.

Mother sat on the deck and rested. Way Ping looked at Father and said, "Was I a bad Master of the Boat, Father?"

"No, little Son, a good Master you were, for when trouble came, you remembered what I had told you of winds and sails. And the boat knew your voice and did as you wished. Come now. I have brought fish balls and bean greens for supper. Come, Master of Boats."

Dorothy Rowe

105

Kintu

Magic

Kintu was a boy who lived in Africa with his father and mother and his five brothers and sisters. They lived in a big mud house with a pointed straw roof. It looked like a large beehive. It was the largest of a bunch of houses in the jungle, for Kintu's father, Kitomba, was a chief and so a very important person.

Kintu and his two brothers and three sisters were very busy children. They spent their days learning to do the things they would need to do when they were older.

106

Kintu had to learn more than anyone else, because he was the oldest son and would one day be chief. A chief must know, for one thing, how to throw a spear just right. Every day Kintu practiced for hours, throwing his spear at a red circle painted on a tree.

Kintu learned how to play the drums. With the palms of his hands he could make them talk as drums do in Africa, when messages are sent from village to village.

"Look out, look out!" say the drums, beating deeply. "An enemy tribe is coming down the river." Or they say, "Look out, look out! An angry storm is coming from the east."

A chief's son must be able to dance to the drums as well as play them. Kintu learned many kinds of dances. For one of them his father let him have a beautiful headdress of bright red feathers. Kintu liked that dance the best.

Kintu learned many other things, too. He learned how to make heads for the spears, how to make a fire with two sticks, and how to climb trees almost as fast as a monkey. He learned, too, the things that are good to eat in the jungle.

107

At night after supper the people of the village would gather around a fire and talk or sing. The oldest men of the tribe told of hunting in the jungle when lions were fiercer and elephants were bigger than any found nowadays. Kintu, sitting beside his father, would shiver and try not to listen to their tales because he was afraid of the jungle.

Sometimes at night Kintu would lie awake and listen to the strange sounds made by the wild creatures in the jungle. He would lie on his hard earthen bed and would shake with fright, for he knew that when he was older, Kitomba would want him to hunt in the jungle. It would never do for a chief's son to be afraid!

Kintu was worried, and at last he decided to go to the witch doctor and ask him for a charm to make him braver. So one morning, after breakfast, he left his brothers and sisters, and all by himself went to the witch doctor's house.

The witch doctor was very old and very wise. He looked down at Kintu without smiling, and Kintu would have shaken in his shoes, if he'd had any shoes.

108

"Chief's son," said the witch doctor, "why have you come to see me?"

"Witch doctor," began Kintu bravely, "I am in great trouble. I am afraid of the jungle!" He stopped, but the witch doctor said nothing, so he went on. "Yes, I'm afraid of it—its fierce beasts, its noises, and its huge trees! I don't even like the way it smells. How can I ever be a great chief like my father when I am such a coward?"

Kintu hung his head and waited for the witch doctor to say something.

"This is bad!" said the witch doctor. "I must think."

He sat down and pulled his big black hat over his nose and thought. Kintu leaned against the wall and watched him without a sound.

After several minutes the witch doctor stood up, pushing back his hat. Still without smiling, he looked down at Kintu.

"Chief's son," he said, "I believe I have a charm for you." He took something out of a red bowl and put it into Kintu's hand.

"Take this," he said, "and tomorrow, when the sun is at its highest, walk three hundred steps into the jungle toward the east. After you have walked for three hundred steps, plant this charm at the foot of the first baobab tree you find. When you have buried it, say these words—"

(But what the words were I cannot tell you, for they were black magic and a secret.)

"In the jungle? All by myself?" asked Kintu in a small voice.

"All by yourself, Chief's son," said the witch doctor firmly.

Kintu walked slowly home. Once he stopped and opened his hand to see what the charm was like. It was nothing but a dry stone of a fruit and did not look as though it had much magic in it. But the witch doctor had said it had magic, and Kintu believed him.

That evening Kintu could not eat his supper. Very late that night he lay awake and listened to the jungle sounds, which seemed louder than ever. "Afraid, afraid, afraid," they seemed to say to Kintu.

In the Jungle

The next day dawned bright and very hot. When the sun was at its highest and everybody else had gone to sleep under the trees, Kintu took his spear and the witch doctor's charm, and went quietly into the jungle.

As Kintu walked he said, "One, two, three," and forgot to be afraid. The farther he walked, the darker and deeper the jungle grew. He had a hard time pushing his way through the vines which hung from every tree.

"Two hundred eighty," said Kintu, jumping over a fallen tree, "two hundred eighty-one, eighty-two, eighty-three. . . ." On his right something gave a squeak and jumped out of sight.

At last he had taken the three hundred steps, and he began to seek for a baobab tree. There were gum trees and rubber trees and many other kinds of trees, but there was not one baobab tree in sight.

Kintu sighed. His head was hot and the palms of his hands felt cold. But he just could not turn back till he had buried the magic fruit stone.

So he went farther and farther into the jungle, and at last he came upon an enormous baobab tree standing all by itself in a clearing.

Kintu felt safer when he saw this. He made a hole with the head of his spear and buried the charm. After that he said the words of black magic which the witch doctor had taught him.

When Kintu had buried the charm, he took his spear and started back. It had taken him a long time to find the baobab tree, and now it was late in the day.

On and on went Kintu, among flowers and great ferns and tall, dark trees. He knew that he had lost his way, and that so far the magic had not worked, because he felt more frightened than ever. He wished he had never worried about being a coward and had not gone to the witch doctor.

Kintu began to cry quietly, because he was sure that he would never see his family again. He stopped walking and stood very still among the great ferns. He was afraid that any direction he went would be the wrong direction.

Then, all at once, quite near, he heard a sound like that of thick cloth being torn in two. The snarl of a leopard!

Now Kintu did not think standing still a good thing to do any more. Spear in hand, he began to run faster than he had ever run before.

Ahead of him six little monkeys, who also had heard the snarl of the leopard, went running and leaping along even faster than Kintu. They seemed like friends, and Kintu followed them.

When the monkeys came to a huge tree hung with vines, they climbed up one after another. Kintu went right after them as fast as he could go.

Up and up Kintu climbed, with his spear between his strong teeth, and his fingers and toes holding tight to the vines. He pulled himself up and up until he nearly reached the top of the big tree.

Then he sat down on a big branch with his spear across his knees. He was hot and out of breath, but he felt a little safer.

Soon the moon came up, big and round above the trees. Each leaf was shining in its light, and the rings that Kintu wore on his ankle looked like gold.

The Leopard

Hours passed. The moon was high in the sky. Kintu, too tired to think of fear any longer, settled himself against the tree trunk and slept near the monkeys.

Kintu must have slept there a long time. When the excited voices of the monkeys woke him, he saw that the moon had set and the world was as black as the inside of a pocket.

He looked down, wondering what was wrong. At first he saw nothing.

Then a shiver of fear ran up Kintu's back. Below him he saw two small lights, side by side, which did not move. He knew they were the eyes of an animal watching him.

Squealing and scolding, the monkeys bounded along the branches into another tree and disappeared. There at black midnight Kintu faced real danger, alone.

Once more he heard the low sound like cloth being torn, the snarl which had so frightened him at dusk. The leopard had found him after all.

The two lights moved a little. Kintu knew that the animal was getting ready to spring.

Then the eyes leaped forward. There was the swish of a heavy body flying through the air, the thud of it hitting against the tree, and the sound of sharp claws tearing wood. The leopard was climbing the tree toward Kintu.

It was no use to be afraid now. Something would have to be done, and quickly too.

Swiftly and quietly Kintu stood up on the branch. He held on to the trunk firmly with his left hand, and in his right he raised the spear high above his shoulder.

116

He could hardly see the leopard climbing toward him, but he would have to take a chance.

"Now or never," said Kintu in a small voice, and hurled the spear.

Then there was the thud of a soft, heavy weight falling upon the earth. After that there were no more sounds at all, and Kintu knew that the leopard would not trouble him again. Not this one, anyway! How glad he was, now, that his father had made him practice hurling the spear day after day!

"I surely won't sleep again," said Kintu, and slept.

Drumbeats

The next time Kintu woke up it was morning. Long fingers of early sunlight came through the leaves. Every bird was singing as though he had to sing louder than any other bird. The world was golden and fresh and wet with dew.

Kintu looked for his spear and wondered if he had dropped it. Then he remembered about the leopard. Quickly he climbed down the vines.

There, at the foot of the tree, lay the leopard, so beautiful with its golden and dark-spotted fur that Kintu was sorry he had killed it. But when he looked closer and saw the cruel white teeth and the shining claws half hidden in the soft paws, he was sorry no longer.

"It is better to kill than to be killed," said Kintu. And pulling his spear from the leopard's hide, he started off once more to seek his village. As he walked along he waved his spear and sang, "I am not afraid!"

The wild creatures watching him, knew that this was true.

"He is not afraid," sang all the birds together.

118

"He is not afraid," chattered the noisy monkeys.

The leopards saw him, too, as they hid among the ferns. "No, he is not afraid," they said and turned away, feeling fear themselves.

Then something made Kintu stop quite still in his tracks and listen hard. Far, far to the right of him, there was a sound in the air. Yes! It was drumbeats that he heard, and they were saying: "Chief Kitomba's oldest son has disappeared. Has he been seen? Has he been seen?"

And then, still farther away, to his left, the drums of another village replied: "Chief Kitomba's son has not been seen. Chief Kitomba's son has not been seen."

Kintu knew that the first drums were the drums of his village. If he turned to the right and followed their sound, he would find his way home.

He could not go fast enough. He ran and bounded high in the air, swinging his ·spear and yelling for joy. But he did not forget to stop now and then and scratch the bark of a tree with his spearhead. When he got back to the village, he would ask some of the men to get the leopard for him. And he wanted them to be sure to find it.

119

There was a shout behind him suddenly, and turning he saw his father running toward him between the trees.

"Father!" cried Kintu, throwing down his spear and leaping into Chief Kitomba's arms.

"I was lost! I spent the night in a tree, I killed a leopard, and I'm not afraid," said Kintu all in one breath.

"You are alive and safe, my son! You are not hurt?" asked Chief Kitomba quickly.

"No, but I am very, very hungry," replied Kintu.

Kintu's mother was so glad to see him alive and unhurt that she cooked a special pudding just for him. Then she stood over him and watched to see that he ate it all.

His brothers and sisters sat round him in a circle, their mouths hanging open a little, and listened to the story of his night in the jungle. He had to tell it three times.

The Celebration

All the people of the village were so glad to see Kintu again that Chief Kitomba said, "Kindle the bonfires. Bring out the big drums. We shall have a celebration as soon as the leopard is brought to the village."

"A celebration!" shouted everybody, and ran to get wood for the bonfires. Half a dozen men followed the marks Kintu had made on the trees to the place where the leopard lay under a tall tree. Cutting down a small tree, they tied the heavy animal to it.

Then putting the tree over their right shoulders, the men walked, singing and laughing, back to the village.

When they had reached it, they went at once to the house of Kintu's father, and set the leopard down beside the door. Everybody came to look at it. They said what a big leopard it was, and what a fine coat it had, and how cruel and terrible it must have been when it was alive.

"Now we will have the celebration," said Chief Kitomba.

Kintu went into the house and put on his beautiful headdress of bright red feathers. Then he walked to the center of the village, where all the tribe had gathered.

Bonfires had been kindled and were burning like five great towers of light and smoke. Half a dozen of the bravest men in the village stood behind the big drums, waiting to play them.

"Come here, my son," said Chief Kitomba, and Kintu went to him. Around his neck his father fastened a string of leopard's teeth, and around his waist he tied a leopard's skin so that the tail hung down behind just as it should.

122

"Now dance," said Chief Kitomba, and Kintu, for the first time in his life, did the Dance of the Good Hunter. For had he not killed the cruel leopard, that creature feared by all men and beasts alike?

To the beating of the drums Kintu moved swiftly, stamping and jumping in the center of a circle. Around him all the people of the village clapped their hands and stamped in time to the music. Drums boomed, ankle rings jingled.

123

Kintu finished his dance with a whoop and a yell. And then everybody danced! After that they asked Kintu to tell them his story.

He told them about climbing the tree after the monkeys and all about the leopard. But he did not tell them why he had gone into the jungle in the first place or about the magic charm. That was a secret between the witch doctor and himself and the baobab tree.

When his story was done, Kintu said good night to all his friends. But before going to his father's house, he went to see the witch doctor.

"Well, Chief's son," said the witch doctor, and he looked down at Kintu without smiling. But this time Kintu was not afraid at all.

"Well, witch doctor," he said, "I am grateful to you. I did all you told me to, and then I got lost. I spent the night in the jungle among the wild creatures. I even killed a leopard. And this morning when I woke up, I found I wasn't a coward any more!"

The witch doctor did not look very much surprised.

Elizabeth Enright

124

The First Lamb

Shepherd Boys

His name was Abd el Karuzeh. His father and his mother said it deep down in their throats so that each part of it sounded almost the same as all the others, like the echo of little stones dropped into a deep well.

It was a big name for a small boy, but he was older than he looked. All the people who live in the caves in the hill country of North Africa are small people.

Abd el Karuzeh was ten years old, and for two years now he had helped herd the village flocks.

Every morning Abd el Karuzeh and the other boys of his age went from cave to cave and called out the sheep and goats of the family or families living there.

Then uphill they all went, following trails which only they could see and climbing hills which only sheep and goats and boys of the mountain country could climb.

One by one Abd el Karuzeh and the other boys rounded up a dozen or more ewes with their lambs. Each boy with his flock stopped on some hillside where the sun had brought a little green out of the rocks and earth. Sheep are stupid creatures, Abd el Karuzeh's father said, and there has to be much food under their very noses—else they will die!

Farther on, where only weeds grew among the rocks, the bigger boys kept the goats.

Still farther, among the crags where one could see hardly any green thing, the boys who were almost men helped the camels to find a little food. They did not come back to the caves every night. Each of those older boys carried a spear, for no one knew when a lion would spring from a rock.

Abd el Karuzeh carried a sharp, pointed knife stuck through his belt. But lions did not often come close to the caves. He had only hyenas to be afraid of—and then only after dark.

Darkness comes quickly in the mountains, once the sun has set. And well Abd el Karuzeh knew that when the shadows of the rocks began to grow blue, he must gather his ewes and their lambs together and hurry down the hill. The sheep made a light sound on the rocks, but a hyena made no sound at all until its strong teeth had broken a lamb's neck.

But Abd el Karuzeh was not thinking of hyenas on one sunny afternoon. He was swinging his bare legs over a huge rock and feeling sorry for himself.

127

Abd el Karuzeh's father was poor—poor even for the people who lived in the caves. He owned only a half-dozen sheep. Therefore he had not, like other fathers, given his son a lamb with which to start a flock of his own.

"You must earn your first lamb," he had replied when the boy asked. But he had turned his face away when he said it, for he loved his son and it was hard to tell him this.

How was any boy to start a flock without even one lamb to call his own? Abd el Karuzeh sat on a big rock and hung his bare legs down its warm sides as he thought.

What could he do to earn a lamb? Abd el Karuzeh asked himself hundreds of times, but there was no answer.

The only way he had ever known a boy to get a lamb was for his father to give it to him. Almost every boy of his age could look at the flock and point out a lamb, or perhaps a ewe and her lamb, that belonged to him.

Abd el Karuzeh knew that the boys loved their sheep. When pink and azure flowers brought color to the hills after the rains, they tied flowers around their sheep's necks and to their legs and fat tails. And on frosty nights when the fires died down and the caves grew cold, the boys crept among their own sheep and lay close to them for warmth.

But what could a boy do to earn a lamb? If he could kill a lion or a leopard and bring the skin to the Headman, then the tribe would be grateful and would give him almost anything—a sheep, a goat, even a camel. But Abd el Karuzeh knew that not many men had killed a leopard and fewer still a lion. Therefore he would have to think of some other way.

Just then Abd el Karuzeh heard a shout, and he looked up to see another shepherd. The sun was already red in the western sky, and the shepherds were rounding up their flocks to return to the caves. Abd el Karuzeh, being one of the youngest boys, did not go as far into the hills as the others, so he waited as they brought down their sheep.

The sun fell lower and lower until the highest crags hid part of it.

"The Headman's sons are late," one shepherd said uneasily, looking up at the hills.

"Do you see them, Abd el Karuzeh?" asked another. "Your eyes are sharp."

Abd el Karuzeh looked across the hillsides, but there was no sign of the two boys and their flock.

The other boys stood waiting for the sons of the Headman. They would have waited for any one of the shepherds, even the poorest. No shepherd boy leaves another alone in the hills after dark, for even men are afraid of the hyena at night.

Where were the two boys? Even the sheep and goats bunched together as though afraid.

130

But what was that? It sounded like the patter of rain on dry leaves. A sigh of relief broke from the boys, and even the flock started milling about as though glad. Hurrying down the path came the Headman's sons and their sheep. But they were not happy boys.

"We have had to leave a lamb," said Fuad, the older of the two.

A Lamb Left Behind

The boys' relief turned to sadness. Not only are his sheep of use to a shepherd, but he loves them as a mother loves a baby. And just as no careful mother will leave her baby, so a good shepherd will not abandon one of his flock in the hills.

"What happened?" asked someone in a low voice, and every boy bent forward, listening.

Feragi, the Headman's younger son, pointed to a big white ewe that kept sniffing the lambs of the flock and bleating softly now and then. She was hunting for a lamb which was not there!

"She-of-the-Quick-Light-Feet went off a little way from the flock," he said, "and I followed to bring her back. When I was but two or three steps from her, I saw a snake among the stones between us, and I hurled a rock at it. I killed the snake, but our ewe, She-of-the-Quick-Light-Feet, was frightened and leaped sideways, knocking her lamb over the cliff."

"Could you not reach it?" Abd el Karuzeh knew the answer before he asked.

132

"No," Fuad replied. "It fell on a narrow ledge that stuck out from the cliff. If we could have got down to it, we could not have climbed back up again. It is a pity too, for She-of-the-Quick-Light-Feet is a good ewe, and her lambs make fine sheep."

"And it was unhurt," Feragi put in.

"It will be hurt soon," Fuad said shortly. "Even now a hyena may have it. Oh, we tried to get it, but the rock snapped under our hands, and the bushes broke under our weight. We were each too big and heavy."

"I thought Fuad was going to fall once," Feragi said.

"It is late and we must get the flock back to the caves before we lose any more," Fuad said, as he started his friends and the animals down the trail.

"A lamb, a fine lamb, alive and unhurt, where a boy might reach it," thought Abd el Karuzeh. It seemed a pity to abandon it to the hyenas.

"*Yah hya ris!* Yes, my captain!"

The shepherds were singing as they always did when returning home at night.

They did not see that Abd el Karuzeh had remained behind them. He stopped short. Back there in the dim evening light was a lamb, a good lamb, unhurt—on a ledge where he might rescue it. Back there, too, there might be hyenas ready to kill a lamb or a boy!

"*Yah hya ris!*" came the shepherds' song. That way lay food, warmth, friends, safety. As Abd el Karuzeh looked after the boys, he saw Fuad go over to a tired lamb, pick it up, and swing it around his neck. He was a good shepherd. He would never have abandoned a lamb if he could have reached it at all.

Suddenly Abd el Karuzeh turned and trotted off into the darkness. One by one the stars came out, and the moon shone with a soft azure light.

"*Yah hya ris!*"

Abd el Karuzeh found himself singing softly as he hurried along. Thinking of the song helped him to forget about hyenas. And when he sang, he could not hear what might run up behind him.

A stone rolled down the hillside, and he began to run faster. Was there really something following him?

134

On and on he ran, with his heart in his throat and his blood pounding in his ears.

His foot sent another stone downhill, and he thought he heard something. He listened hard.

"Baaaaaaaaah!"

Only a lamb—a cold lamb—bleated like that!

"Baaaaaaaaah!"

He followed the sad bleating call. Here was the cliff. Here was the place where Fuad and Feragi had dug their feet into the earth as they tried to find a way down the cliff. And there, looking up at him from below, was the lamb!

Abd el Karuzeh took off his coat. He lay down flat, slid over the cliff, and with his toes felt for a bit of rock to stand on.

Inch by inch the boy crawled down, holding hard to the rock in front of him, his clothes wet with sweat. Time after time the rock beneath one foot or the other broke and went crashing down the mountainside. Only his strong fingers saved him. Fuad had been right. The bushes were too small and the rock too easily broken to have held a larger boy.

At last he stood on the narrow ledge beside the lamb. He picked it up, and it put its head against his shoulder. As he felt its warm wool, he could see in the dim moonlight that there was something dark on its back, and he saw, too, that his fingers were bleeding.

Savage beasts can smell blood a long way off. Abd el Karuzeh moved back against the cliff and peered to the right and left of him. There was no time to lose. The smell of blood would surely bring animals, and quickly.

He put the lamb about his neck as he had seen Fuad do, took off his belt, and tied its feet together.

Climbing down the cliff had been slow, hard work. Climbing up was even slower and harder.

136

He was tired. His bleeding fingers hurt. The lamb about his neck made him feel clumsy. Its feet hit the rock. He could not put his forehead as close to the cliff as he wanted to for safety. If the lamb should grow afraid and try to move, even a little, it might send them both into the dark below.

There might be a hyena jumping at his ankles, or one waiting above to attack him. It seemed forever before his hands reached the flat rock and he crawled up over the top of the cliff.

137

Abd el Karuzeh was not quite sure how far he was from his father's cave. He peered down the long path he must take, and his breath caught in his throat. A gleam of light! Was it a hyena's eyes? Now many gleams! What animals were these?

Then he laughed aloud. Animals' eyes are in pairs, and they are still in the darkness. Each of these lights bobbed up and down in its own way. Hyenas walk softly, too, on padded feet, and Abd el Karuzeh's good ears caught the sound of footsteps almost as soon as he had seen the torches.

"Halloooooo!" he shouted, pulling the last sound out long and high.

"Halloooooo!" came back his father's voice. The rocks rattled beneath his feet as he scampered down the path, but there was no need to go quietly now. No animal, however hungry or savage, attacks men with fire in their hands.

Fuad and Feragi were with the group of men, and their father also. Abd el Karuzeh untied the lamb and placed it in Fuad's hands.

"Why do you do that, Abd el Karuzeh?" the Headman asked.

138

"Did not your boys tell you?" Abd el Karuzeh asked in surprise. "It belongs to you. It is the lamb of your ewe, She-of-the-Quick-Light-Feet."

"It is a lamb my boys left to die," the Headman replied slowly. "Therefore it no longer belongs to us. We could not use its wool with gladness. When it was grown, we could not feel that its lambs were ours." The Headman turned to his son. "Fuad, return the lamb to its owner!"

Tears fell from Abd el Karuzeh's eyes and sank into the lamb's soft wool. It was not manly to cry, he knew, but now not only his fingers hurt, but his heart was very grateful.

"Abd el Karuzeh!" His father spoke sharply, as poor men the world over often do when they are proud of their children. The boy sank on one knee before the Headman and laid his forehead upon the Headman's hand in sign of thanks.

Then, with Fuad on one side and Feragi on the other, and his lamb—his very own lamb—in his arms, Abd el Karuzeh followed the group back to the warmth and safety of the caves.

Louise Stinetorf

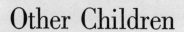

Other Children

Some children live in palaces
Behind an iron gate,
And go to sleep in beds of gold
Whenever it gets late.

And way up north the children live
In houses built of ice,
And think that beds made out of fur
Are really very nice.

In countries where the nights are hot
Without a single breeze,
The children sleep in bamboo beds
That fasten in the trees.

Some day I think I'll travel round
And visit every land,
And learn to speak the language that
Each child can understand.

They'll want to ask me questions then,
And I will ask them others,
Until at last we understand
Like sisters and like brothers.

Helen Wing

Moving On

Success for Little Blacknose

What's the Matter?

Blacknose was a locomotive. He was one of the first locomotives ever built in America. He was not very large, but he could pull five coaches, and that was five times as much as a horse could pull.

The day he made his first run with the coaches behind him had been a great day for little Blacknose. He had been named the *DeWitt Clinton* after a famous man of that time, and many famous people had traveled in his coaches.

Six weeks had passed since then. It was a day in the early fall of 1831. Little Blacknose did not know that, and he would not have cared if he had known it. But he did know that something had waked him up very early. There was a great roaring outside his shed.

142

At first he could not understand what made the noise. But pretty soon, as he listened and wondered, he knew it came from hundreds of people all shouting together. He had never heard so many before, never in his whole engine life! Then he noticed that John Bull was gone.

John Bull was a big locomotive who had just been brought from England. He was much bigger and stronger than little Blacknose, and he was very proud of himself. He was so big that little Blacknose hardly dared to speak to him.

"They have taken him out and left me," thought Blacknose. "It's his big day, and I'm out of it!" Poor little Blacknose! He felt as if he never could get his steam up again.

The shouting grew louder and louder. Little Blacknose could only hear. He could not see what was going on. He had remained in his dark shed for hours and hours, or so he thought.

"No wood! Not even a nibble of coal! No water! No breakfast, no breakfast, no breakfast!"

He was getting very hungry. It was the first time he had not been fed and cared for. It was the first time he had not been needed and used.

143

Suddenly he heard, "Uh, huh, I guess you'll not be so stuck up now!"

It was the old gray horse sticking his homely nose through the window of the shed and making fun of poor little Blacknose. With a loud neigh he went on, "I suppose they'll take you out still —sometimes—on rainy days." A minute later the window was empty.

Then a crew of men came rushing into the shed. They began to push and pull at little Blacknose.

"What can they want with me?" he sadly wondered. And then a terrible feeling shot through his pipes and boiler. He guessed—he knew! They were taking him out for the crowd to laugh at! They would stand him up beside the great new engine from England, and everyone would laugh and point and say how small and queer he was!

144

He wouldn't go. He couldn't go! If only he could stay unnoticed in his small, dark shed! He tried to keep his wheels from turning! It was no use. They were running him out now into the middle of the shouting crowd. He wouldn't look. He couldn't look! And then he noticed the English engine.

A little distance down the track stood John Bull with his steam all up. Flowers were hung around his huge neck, and he looked very great and grand. He had ten bright coaches fastened on behind him, but the coaches were all empty!

"Why doesn't he go? Why are all the people outside the coaches? What is the matter with him?" Blacknose wondered.

Then David Mathew, his own engineer, came pushing his way through the crowd.

"Will even David laugh at me?" thought Blacknose.

But no, David laid a loving hand on the cold boiler of the little engine.

"Fill her up, men," he said to the crew of workmen beside him. "We'll have to use the *DeWitt Clinton* after all."

What a roar went up from the huge crowd!

"Hurrah for the *DeWitt Clinton!*" they cried. "Hurrah for the little American engine! Hurrah, hurrah, hurrah!"

At last little Blacknose dared to look at the crowd. Why, they weren't laughing at him at all! They were cheering and waving. They were shouting for him, just as they always used to do.

For a minute he felt as if a large, fat piece of coal had got stuck in his supply pipe. He felt so very, very queer! A minute later real pieces of coal were falling fast into his poor, empty little firebox. Real shining pieces of coal!

"Breakfast, breakfassssst, breakfassssssst!" he hissed happily. His steam was coming up.

It was the new engine's big day, but they had
to send for him.

"Breakfast, breakfasssssst, breakfassssssssst!"

What was the matter with the English engine?
Couldn't it go? He knew it had run before, when
they gave it a try. He had seen it himself—big
and proud, chugging along with a noisy clang.

"Well, anyway, it isn't going now," he thought.
"Sssssee the empty coachchch-esssss!" he hissed.

What were they doing now? They were taking
the coaches from John Bull, all ten of them. Three
of them were fastened on to Blacknose. Now they
were leading up seven horses. Each horse was
fastened to one of the seven other coaches.
The excursion train was ready, and he was at
its head!

How the people rushed to squeeze into the three coaches behind little Blacknose! What a shouting and pushing there was! The little engine looked back proudly along his train of three.

"All the great people of the land are riding behind me," he noticed. "Only the near-great ride behind the horses."

"Toot, toot, toot!" Such a blowing of the whistle! "Hooray, hooray, hurrah!" Such a shouting from the passengers!

And they were off at last! Just as his wheels began to turn, Blacknose heard an excited neigh from the ugly old gray horse, who was fastened to the first coach behind his three.

"Baby iron beast, if it weren't for you, I'd get to Schenectady first!" the old gray horse neighed. But little Blacknose only laughed.

"Choo, choo, choo! Chew your own smoke!" he cried. "Pretty soon you won't be able even to smell mine! Choo! Choo! Choo!"

And then he noticed the big English engine, looking very sad, and he saw that the flowers around his big smokestack had started to fall to pieces.

148

Such Speed!

"T-double Y-ditty.

Off for Schenectady!" sang little Blacknose.

The wind whistled over his smokestack. The trees flew by. The rails gleamed ahead of him. He had never gone so fast before.

In just forty-six minutes he stood puffing and blowing at the Schenectady end of his track. Now everybody cheered him as they climbed out of his yellow-and-green coaches.

"It's the greatest day of my life!" he heard one man say. "I've never ridden so fast before."

"Such speed!" said another, straightening his tall hat. "Only forty-six minutes from Albany!"

"But where are the horses?" asked a third, speaking to David Mathew.

"I don't see them, sir," answered David, gazing into the distance with his hand over his eyes.

Where were the horses? Twenty-nine minutes later, the first of the horses climbed slowly up the last hill and drew up his coach beside little Blacknose's train of three coaches. It was the old gray horse—all out of breath and oh, so tired!

"So you wanted to get ahead of me! What do you think of engines now?" puffed little Blacknose.

But this time the poor old horse didn't even look at little Blacknose. He shut his eyes and dropped his homely head and tried to rest his tired legs.

When the other horses and coaches had arrived, Blacknose saw the passengers all go off toward Schenectady with the people who had come to meet them.

"They're off to get their coal and water, I suppose," the little engine thought. In two hours he saw them all come back again. The excursion train was ready for the return trip to Albany.

"Te-dick, te-dack,

Let's hurry back!" sang Blacknose.

Never had he run so well. In just thirty-eight minutes he was back at the Albany end of his track, puffing hard but feeling very proud.

"My word!" cried David Mathew, as he climbed down from the little engine. "We've been going nineteen miles an hour!"

"Nineteen miles? Wonderful!" said one of the great men. "I have never known such speed!"

151

"Hurrah for the *DeWitt Clinton!*" cried all the passengers. "Hurrah for the little American engine! Hooray, hooray, hooray!"

All this time the locomotive from England stood quiet and unnoticed near by. He looked very sad, Blacknose thought, and he almost felt sorry for him. Then suddenly he found that the English engine was trying to talk to him. He had only a little steam left, so his voice was very throaty and low.

"My-dear-chap-very-kind-of-you," John Bull was saying. Little Blacknose could just make it out.

"I didn't know we had met," puffed back Blacknose. But the minute he said it, he was sorry. The poor English engine looked so sad!

"Sorry-I-was-mean. Very-thankful-now," he whispered. "You-saved-my-excursion."

"Oh, don't thank me," Blacknose said. "I've had the run of my life! By the way, what was the matter with you, anyway?"

"Something-wrong-in-my-supply-pipe," John Bull whispered. "Couldn't-repair-me. Don't-understand-strangers-over-here. I'm-English-you-know!"

"Oh, are you?" said Blacknose. Why, the Englishman was a nice chap, after all! "Well, I'll be glad to help you any time you need me. I hope your supply pipe will be better soon."

Little Blacknose was very happy as they ran him away to rest.

"Success, successsssssssss, successsssssssss!" he breathed gently, letting off his steam.

"Success, successsssssssss, successsssssssss!"

As for the ugly old gray horse, he hadn't even come in sight!

Hildegarde H. Swift

153

Birthday Train

A Strange Present

School had closed for two months, and a week from Monday was Dan Summers' birthday. His father had just asked him what he wanted for his birthday present.

"I want a train ride," said Dan.

Dan would be nine years old on his birthday, but never in his life had he ridden on a railroad train. He had often seen trains when he was traveling in the automobile with his father and mother. They had waited at railroad crossings while long freight trains of box cars, tank cars, flat cars, and a caboose went rumbling past.

He had seen streamline passenger trains going smoothly across the high bridge over the river.

The streamliners were bright with red and orange paint and looked from far away like shiny toy trains. And every time he had seen them, Dan had wished he could have a train ride.

"Where do you want to go on your train ride?" asked his mother.

Dan said, "I want to go to Sunny Hills." That was near his grandfather's farm.

"Oh, ho," laughed Mr. Summers. "You are really going to get two birthday presents in one, I see. A train ride and a visit to the farm!"

Dan smiled and his face got a little red. "Well, how about it?" he said.

"You wouldn't want to go on the streamliner, I suppose?" His father smiled. "A seat on that train must be reserved. I'll try to reserve a seat for your birthday."

He went to the telephone. When he came back, he said, "Everything is O.K. Your seat is reserved for a week from Monday."

"Oh, thanks, Dad," said Dan. "I really didn't hope I could go on the streamliner."

155

"Now you'd better write to Grandmother," said Mrs. Summers, "and ask if she is willing to have you come for a visit that week."

Dan wrote the letter at once, and the answer came very quickly. Of course Grandmother was willing. So the morning of his birthday Dan and his parents got into the automobile and drove to the railway station.

Dan had been in the station before when they went to meet his grandparents. He knew how the big building with its high, shiny walls looked. And he had listened to the loud voice of the man who told when the trains were leaving and where they were going. His voice came out of a loud speaker high up near the roof, and you could hear it all over the station.

Mr. Summers went to the window where the tickets were sold, and bought a ticket for Dan. On it were the numbers of his car and of his seat.

"Remember to hold on to your ticket," Father said as he gave it to Dan. "You can't get to Sunny Hills without it."

Dan took out his wallet and put the ticket safely inside it.

156

Then Dan stopped to look at the model of an old-time locomotive he had noticed in a glass case.

Soon the train to Sunny Hills was called, and the Summers family followed the crowd of people into a long, brightly lighted tunnel. When at last they came out of the tunnel, there was the train!

It was a red-and-orange train just like the ones Dan had seen crossing the high bridge near town. Only now it did not look like a toy at all. It looked longer than a freight train to Dan. It stretched all the way through the station and out the other side. And there the huge engine stood with little feathers of steam coming out of the top of it.

Dan thought the man who ran that engine was the luckiest man in the world.

157

All Aboard!

The conductor was standing beside the train, and Mr. Summers took Dan up to him. "This is Dan," he said. "Dan is taking his first train ride. It's his birthday, and he wanted the train ride for his birthday present."

"Then we'll see to it that he enjoys his present," said the conductor. "Let me see your ticket, please."

Dan pulled out his wallet and showed his ticket to the conductor.

"To Sunny Hills," said the conductor. "That's a good long ride. We get there at five o'clock."

He spoke to the porter on the platform. "This young man has seat number nineteen."

The porter, who wore a white coat and had a friendly smile, took Dan's suitcase into the car.

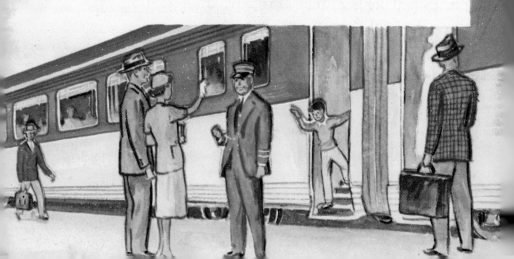

Dan waved good-by to his father and mother. Then he followed the porter along the aisle to seat number nineteen.

When he looked out of the window, there were his father and mother standing on the station platform, looking up at him. His mother was trying to tell him something, but he could not hear a word. She was making her lips move in a careful way so that he might guess what she was saying.

All at once he had an idea. It would be just like Mother to wonder if he still had his ticket.

Dan reached into his pocket, pulled out his wallet, and held up the ticket for her to see. She smiled and nodded.

Suddenly the train was moving. There was no noise, but all at once Dan's parents, still waving to him, disappeared from sight. So Dan knew the train must have started. He put his ticket back in the wallet and looked around him.

159

Most of the seats were taken. Some men were reading newspapers, and a woman was sewing. Dan didn't see how anyone could read or sew while riding on a train. There was too much to see!

He turned back to his window, and then he got really excited. They were coming to the bridge. Dan had forgotten that this train would really go across the railroad bridge just like the trains he had watched.

Now they were going across. Far below him Dan could see the river. It was just a silver ribbon. He could see no track at all. It was as if the train were floating in air. When they were over the bridge, Dan felt better. He'd rather have good hard ground under his train!

After a while the conductor took his ticket. He asked Dan if he was enjoying his birthday present, and Dan said, "Yes, sir."

A few minutes after that, the porter stopped beside Dan and said, "I understand, sir, that this ride is a birthday present."

Dan said, "Yes, sir, it is."

"Perhaps you'd like to see more of the train," said the porter. "Don't you want to go up front to the baggage car with me? I have some things to take care of up there, and I'd be delighted to have you along."

Dan didn't say a word. He just got up and followed the porter. They went through car after car. Dan thought they must have walked a mile or more. In one car there were tables, and Dan remembered that his father had given him a dollar and had said, "You'll need that for a meal on the train."

At last they came to a car that was different from all the others. It had only a few windows and no seats. It was like the inside of a store-house. In it were hundreds of suitcases and boxes all carefully piled and marked. There were men sorting the pieces of baggage.

The porter asked them about a suitcase that had been put on the wrong train.

One of the men looked over everything that was in the baggage car, but he could not find the missing suitcase.

"It's not on this train," he said.

And the porter replied, "Well, that's that."

He started back through the train, and Dan followed him. When they came again to the dining car, Dan could smell things cooking, and suddenly he was very hungry. Several people were now sitting at the tables. So when the head waiter nodded, Dan took a seat.

He looked a long time at the list of things to eat. There were some he had never seen, such as boiled lobster or plum pudding with tangerine sauce. It was hard to decide what he wanted most.

"Write it here, sir," said the waiter, giving him a paper and pencil.

Dan felt very grown-up as he wrote this list:

Turkey sandwich with new peas
Glass of milk
Apple pie

The waiter came and took away the paper, and soon brought Dan what he had asked for.

162

Dan thought it was great fun to sit in the dining car, eating a good meal while the landscape slid past the windows.

The train was going very fast. Once when it sped around a curve, Dan could see the engine puffing bravely far ahead of him.

After lunch Dan went back to his own car and sat listening to the radio, which was playing soft music. Everyone looked sleepy, and Dan began to get sleepy, too. He got up several times and went down the aisle to the end of the car for a drink of ice water. It helped to keep him awake. He'd rather not miss any part of his birthday ride.

163

Thanks for a Good Ride

After a long time and after about the seventh cup of ice water, the porter came to Dan and said, "Sunny Hills is the next stop, sir. I'll have your suitcase ready when you get off."

At once Dan was wide awake. He sat up straight and began to watch the landscape closely. Soon he could see the two hills which, Grandfather always said, looked like a camel's humps. The train rounded a curve and began to slow down. Dan got up and went out to the platform at the end of the car. There was the porter, and he had Dan's suitcase.

The train stopped, and the porter opened the door and went down the steps first. "Watch your step, sir," he said to Dan.

"Thank you very much for the good ride," said Dan. And then he had an idea!

On the other side of the gate he could see his grandparents. He waved to them, but he thought they wouldn't mind waiting a few minutes because of his idea. Quickly he set his suitcase down and started on a run toward the engine.

164

It was a long train. Dan's short legs went faster than they had ever gone before. At last he stood beside the engine. Its mighty drive wheels reached far above his head. It hissed as if it were talking to itself. From the cab the engineer looked down at Dan.

"I just wanted you to know that I had a fine ride," said Dan. "It was my first train ride, and I liked it."

The engineer stuck his head farther out of his cab window and looked back at the train.

"We have a minute, Bud," he said to Dan. "Don't you want to come up?"

Dan could hardly believe his ears, but he lost no time. He just made for the steps at the side of the engine and started to climb. In a few seconds there he was inside the engine—the engine of his very own birthday train.

It was as hot as a furnace there, but Dan was sure it was the most wonderful spot in the world.

Everything was clean and shiny. From the number of things in front of the engineer, Dan thought it must take a long time to learn how to be an engineer. He wanted to ask what controlled the speed and the brakes and other things. But of course there wasn't time for that.

"I'm going to be an engineer when I grow up," Dan said.

"In that case," said the engineer, "you may ring the bell. And as soon as you've done that, you have to get out of here as fast as you got in."

"Oh, thanks!" said Dan.

And the engineer let him ring the bell.

Then Dan was climbing down out of the engine as fast as he went up. He hardly had time to turn around before the train began to move. The engineer lifted his hand to Dan, and Dan lifted his in return.

Then he just stood there, counting the cars as they sped past him. The seventh was the dining car, and at last his own car came by. The porter was on the platform fastening the door, and he waved good-by to Dan. Then the car swept past, and there was the conductor, and he smiled at Dan. And still Dan just stood there, while his birthday train traveled away on its steel track, growing smaller and smaller.

Finally a voice behind him said, "Well, here's the boy who belongs to that suitcase!"

There were Grandmother and Grandfather, looking delighted to see him. Dan gave them each a big hug because he was glad to see them, too. Besides he was just remembering, now that the train was gone, that Grandmother made very, very good cakes. And this was his birthday.

Doris Gates

Highways Then and Now

Long, long ago, before there were roads anywhere in this country, there were paths, or
trails. The Indians made the paths as they went
back and forth in the wilderness between their
villages. They cut down brush and trees. They
kept the paths clear and open.

Later the first white people who came to this
country followed the trails the Indians had
made. Sometimes the white settlers rode on
horses or used them for carrying loads, but the
horses followed the same trails as the foot
travelers.

The paths always went the way the land
went. They led uphill and down. They went
around rocky humps and across streams. Sometimes they followed the windings of rivers to the
safest and easiest passes, or gaps, between the
mountains.

168

The famous Wilderness Road grew from a trail through the Cumberland Gap. It was this road over which Daniel Boone led the first settlers into the wild country called Kentucky, west of the mountains. Indian moccasins had worn it smooth long before Daniel Boone and other white men followed it.

All through Kentucky and the country north of the Ohio River there were many Indian trails. From some of the large Indian villages, paths led in all directions like the spokes of a wheel.

When the settlers began to use carts and wagons to move their household goods, they needed roads. Some of these roads were just double paths made wider by the wagon wheels. But other roads had to be built by hard work. Trees had to be cut down and wet places filled in. Some of the first roads were given a hard surface of gravel or of logs laid close together.

169

Many of the new roads followed the old Indian trails. The white men found that they could not choose any better routes than those used by the Indians.

People who used the new roads had to pay some money. This was called paying a toll. There were tollgates at the points where the toll was to be paid.

After a while roads were built that could be used without paying toll. The first great road of this kind was the Cumberland Road from Maryland to Ohio.

These early roads were not paved, except where they passed through cities. A dirt or gravel surface was easier and safer for horses than a paved surface.

Not till men began using automobiles instead of wagons and coaches, did roads finally become the paved highways we know today.

For automobiles, roads with a hard surface were needed. And as more and more automobiles traveled the highways, wider roads were needed. When men rebuilt the roads for paving, they also widened them, did away with sharp curves, cut down steep hills, and filled valleys. They put up route numbers and safety signs, and lights at crossroads to control traffic.

Automobile highways now cross our land in all directions from Maine to California and from Florida to Washington. The old Cumberland Road grew into a highway that now stretches from Washington, D. C., to California.

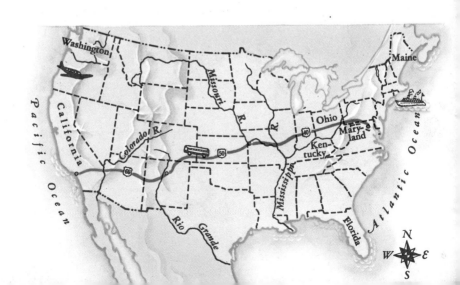

As you ride smoothly along such a cement highway, it is hard to remember that it was once a narrow winding path. It is hard to remember that Indians went silently along it, watching the forest closely on either side.

It is hard to remember that over such paths, then growing into roads, the early settlers followed Daniel Boone and other leaders into the western wilderness and across the prairies.

But it is good to remember such things. It makes you feel closer to the brave people of long ago who built our country out of that wilderness.

Doris Gates

Roads

A road might lead to anywhere—
    To harbor towns and quays,
Or to a witch's pointed house
    Hidden by bristly trees.

It might lead past the tailor's door,
    Where he sews with needle and thread,
Or by Miss Pim the milliner's,
    With her hats for every head.

It might be a road to a great, dark cave
    With treasure and gold piled high,
Or a road with a mountain tied to its end,
    Blue-humped against the sky.

Oh, a road might lead you anywhere—
    To Mexico or Maine.
But then, it might just fool you and—
    Lead you back home again!

Rachel Field

The Horseless Carriage

Father's Surprise

"It's funny that your father doesn't say what train he's taking from Chicago," said Mrs. Marshall, as she folded a letter that had just come from Mr. Marshall.

"I'd like to meet him at the station," said Nan. "He's been in Chicago a whole month."

Nan missed her father. He often went away on trips, but never before had he stayed so long. Since he had not told them on what train he would arrive, Nan decided to ride down to the station on her bicycle to meet all the trains. It was Saturday and there was no school.

But no one in the Marshall family met any trains that day! Long before the first train arrived at eleven-forty, Jimmie came leaping up the steps and slammed the front door behind him so that the old house shook.

"Mother! Nan! Oh, come quick!" he shouted. "Come on out, everybody!" Again the front door slammed.

Mother sighed. "What has got into that boy?"

174

She hurried outside as fast as she could, and Nan ran after her. Everything looked quite the same as always. What could Jimmie mean?

Then Mother and Nan went down the front walk to the gate. There they could see Jimmie running up the street and waving his arms about in great excitement. They stopped still and looked with all their eyes.

Down the street came one of those queer new horseless carriages that people were talking about. It was moving slowly along, and it made a chugging sound. It was the very first horseless carriage that Nan or her mother had ever seen. Of course they had read about them in the papers and had seen pictures of them. "Automobiles" people called them.

This one was really coming toward them and moving smoothly along.

Then Mrs. Marshall gave a gasp. "Your father is steering it!" she cried.

Mr. Marshall sat very upright on the front seat. He was watching the road carefully and giving all his attention to what he had to do. A crowd of boys were running along behind the car.

"Get a horse!" they shouted.

Nan could hardly believe her eyes. But just then the horseless carriage turned in at the Marshall gate and came to a stop beside them.

"Well, how do you like it?" asked Mr. Marshall.

"I never in all my life!" Mother cried.

Jimmie and Nan wanted to know everything. Yes, the automobile would really go, their father told them. Hadn't they just seen it?

Yes, it did belong to them, and if Mother was willing, they could go for a ride sometime, but not now. Father wanted some breakfast.

When Mother heard the word "breakfast," she hurried into the house. It was a relief to get back to everyday living after this upsetting start of the day. What would Father do next? Even at his age, he was more of a boy than Jimmie.

When Father was seated at the table with coffee and eggs before him, Mother said firmly, "James, do you think it is safe?"

"I've been running it around Chicago for nearly a month," said her husband. "Of course, I'm careful not to go over twenty miles an hour."

"Twenty miles an hour!" gasped Mother. "Why, that's dreadful!"

But Jimmie and Nan thought it would be fun.

Father said that after he had been down to his office, he would take Nan and Jimmie for their first ride, that is, if Mother was willing.

Mother was not at all willing, but she knew she had better be silent about that if there was to be any peace in the family.

Their First Ride

It was five o'clock when Nan and Jimmie climbed into the waiting car. Jimmie made the horn blow until Mother begged him to stop. Father had to take a crank and go to the front of the automobile to start the engine. He whirled and whirled the crank until, all of a sudden, the car came alive and began to shake all over.

Nan looked anxious. Father hurried around and wiggled some queer things by the steering wheel. The engine kept on going, but the car did not shake so much, and Nan felt better.

"Now don't go far and don't be late," warned Mother anxiously. "I'll not have a peaceful minute, James, till you are all safe back home."

178

"Don't you worry," they called.

"I certainly shall!" she answered, as they turned out of the gate.

Father pushed several things in and out and changed a thing he called the gears, and then they drove along smoothly through the town.

It seemed very strange to Nan not to have a horse in front of them. It seemed to her as if she were going to bounce right out into the road.

Jimmie was silent, giving close attention to everything that Father did.

"Will you teach me to drive it?" he asked.

"Sometime soon," said Father, "but you'd better wait a little. These things are still pretty new. They'll be safer as time goes on."

This one was safe enough to suit Jimmie and Nan. Mile after mile it carried them through the soft spring evening. It seemed to Nan as though it ate up the road ahead, so swiftly did it speed along.

"Now," said Father, "we must turn toward home, or Mother will think we've skidded off the road or had some other accident."

179

They were spinning along the road toward home and supper when, all of a sudden, the car began to run slowly and more slowly. ·Father seemed worried.

Nan looked ahead. There was something in the road. It was an old farm horse pulling his wagon home after a hard day's work.

Mr. Marshall stopped his car and waited by the side of the road. But the old farm horse had lifted his heavy old head and was tossing it about. Nan could see the whites of his eyes. He had decided not to go past this strange beast by the side of the road.

"Get up, Dobbin!" shouted the farmer behind him.

It did no good. The farmer jumped from the wagon and ran to the horse's head. He tried to control Dobbin and to lead him gently toward his barn.

180

But old Dobbin would have nothing of that. He tossed his head and leaped about like a large rocking horse.

At last the farmer turned him down a quiet lane and tied him to a post. Then the man came back to have a look at this new machine.

"I've heard of those automobiles," he said to Mr. Marshall, "but this is the first one I've seen. How do you like it?"

"They're the greatest invention of the age," said Mr. Marshall. "You'll all be running around in them in a few years."

The farmer laughed and said there'd likely be a good many people in the hospital first.

It was time for the Marshalls to be getting home, and Mr. Marshall climbed out of the car to start the engine. He took out his crank and gave several good hard turns to it. But the engine would not start. Mr. Marshall looked worried, and then he cranked and cranked some more. But the new automobile just stood there.

Mr. Marshall opened up the front part of the car. He called to Jimmie to bring him a screw driver, which he would find under the seat.

Jimmie handed his father the screw driver and then watched anxiously while Mr. Marshall tightened several little screws. Then Mr. Marshall cranked some more. Nothing happened.

It was getting very dark now. So Jimmie went with the farmer up the road to his house to get a lantern.

The Old and the New

Back at the Marshall house Mrs. Marshall was very much worried. She kept going to look out of the window. No sign of the automobile! She kept stopping her work to listen. No sound of a chugging machine!

"They must certainly have had an accident," she kept thinking. "What should I do?"

Then she went to the telephone to ask friends if they had any news of her family. Each house she called had the same answer. Mr. Marshall had been seen speeding down the road west of the town. No one had seen him come back.

Everyone was much interested to hear about the new automobile and anxious to help, but no one knew what to do.

182

Mrs. Marshall went silently back to her mending. Eight o'clock came and went. Nine o'clock came and went. Another dreadful hour!

At ten o'clock the sound of a horse's hoofs on the silent street reached Mrs. Marshall's ears. "It might be some messenger from the family," she thought, as she hurried down the street to meet the slow pounding of the horse's hoofs. Several of her neighbors joined her.

Clop, clop, clop! Nearer came the sound of hoofs.

"James!" gasped Mrs. Marshall as she stopped short in the street.

A big white horse was pulling Mr. Marshall's new automobile. Inside it sat Mr. Marshall and Jimmie, with Nan asleep between them.

In another minute Nan was in her mother's arms, and everybody was talking and laughing.

"These new inventions!" roared one neighbor, doubling over with laughter.

"They're wonderful when they work," laughed another.

Mrs. Marshall did not think it funny. All she wanted was to know that her family was safe and sound. But Mr. Marshall was laughing as hard as anyone as he led the big white horse into the barn for the night.

"Hay is better than gasoline, isn't it, old fellow?" he said. "But just you wait. Give these new inventions a little more time."

The next day Mr. Marshall found out what was the trouble. He had run out of gasoline.

Soon he was driving the car all over the town and was inviting all his friends to ride. By afternoon he even got Mother to go, but he had to promise not to run faster than ten miles an hour.

"And that's fast enough for anybody," she said.

Caroline D. Emerson

Dick Dawson Travels

By Trailer

For days the Dawson family had been busy getting their trailer ready. Mr. Dawson, who worked in a garage and knew all there is to know about automobiles, had built the trailer himself. Of course the men in the machine shop had helped, but Mr. Dawson had done most of it right in his own back yard. Sometimes he had let Dick help him.

Now the time for vacation was at hand, and the Dawson family was looking forward to a long trip in the new trailer.

It was like a little house or apartment on wheels. It had a stove and an icebox and a place to wash dishes. It had cupboards and closets and seats that made up into comfortable beds. And there were even curtains and a carpet.

185

At last the day came to start on their vacation. Mr. Dawson fastened the trailer on behind the family car. Mrs. Dawson got into the front seat of the car with the baby beside her. Dick, of course, got into the trailer.

But they had driven hardly five miles on their route when something went wrong with the car. The motor began to miss.

"It's most likely the carburetor," said Mr. Dawson. "The weight of the trailer makes the motor work differently. I thought I'd fixed that carburetor so it would be all right. But I guess I'll have to work on it a little more."

The place where the car had stalled was right beside a small airfield. It was the kind of field where pilots take people up in small planes and teach them how to fly. There were a hangar and smooth runways and signals just as at a big airport.

"May I go over to the airfield until you finish with the carburetor?" Dick asked.

"Yes," said Mr. Dawson, "but be careful of the traffic when you go across the highway. When I'm ready, I'll honk for you."

186

Dick went cautiously across the highway and straight into the field. He walked toward the hangar, where he saw many bright little planes with shiny propellers sitting like dragonflies, ready and anxious to shoot into the blue sky.

While he stood looking longingly at the planes, a tall man came by. He stopped and smiled at Dick standing all alone and gazing at the planes as if he loved them.

"Do you want a ride, Sonny?" asked the tall man.

Dick nodded. It was too good to believe, he thought, but still he was sure he had heard the man say it.

"I'll have to ask my father first," he said.

"O. K.," said the man. "Where is he?"

Dick pointed to the car and ran to the highway, calling, "Dad, Dad, can I go up in an airplane? The man invited me. Can I?"

"Say 'may I,' Dick. 'May I go?'" said Mrs. Dawson. "But of course not. There might be an accident."

Mr. Dawson was more used to airplanes than his wife was. "I think it would be quite safe," he said. "After all, he's going to do it sometime, and he's ten years old now. Won't you change your mind?"

Poor Mrs. Dawson! What could she do with both Dick and her husband begging her? At last she said, "All right," and Dick raced back to the field. The Dawsons watched as he walked toward the plane beside the tall pilot, and in a moment they saw the little plane taxi down the field and rise into the blue sky.

Mrs. Dawson tried to keep it in sight, but there were many little yellow planes in the sky, and soon she could not tell one from another. She carried the baby back to the trailer, pulled the curtains so that he would go to sleep, and tried to think that everything would be all right.

188

By Airplane

During this time Dick was having a wonderful ride. The motor of the plane sounded loud and strong. Far below he could see the highway, just as if it were marked out on a map, and the car and trailer looking no bigger than peanuts.

Then the land seemed to tip up, and the fields looked like a patchwork quilt. The plane was turning, and now the hills came into sight. They seemed to flatten out as the plane got close to them and then went zooming over them. They looked to Dick just like the mountains on the map he had made at school.

Away off to the right was a wide stretch of silver shining in the sun. It was the river. Soon they had crossed that too and were above another valley with more patchwork fields.

Then all at once the motor sounded queer. It missed a few times. Then it stopped completely. Dick looked back at the pilot. His face looked unhappy, but he did not appear to be scared. So Dick decided not to be scared, either.

Then it seemed to Dick that the ground was rising up toward them. He thought this must mean just one thing. The pilot was landing the plane. Down, down they dropped, and now Dick could see a grove and a field below them. Then there was a gentle bump and they were down.

"Something wrong with the gas line, Sonny," said the pilot, as he got out some tools.

Dick's thoughts went to his family, waiting for him beside Route 46. "How long will it take to fix it?" Dick was a bit worried.

"It may take quite a while," said the pilot.

"I have to get back to the airfield," said Dick. "My family's waiting for me there to go on our vacation."

"That's right. They'll be expecting you soon," said the pilot. "I'll tell you what we'll do. Over there is the highway, and near that orange grove is a country store. We'll telephone to the airfield and send a messenger to your folks. Then you can take the bus back to the field. How does that sound?"

Dick nodded. "O. K., only I haven't any money for the bus."

190

The man smiled and reached into his pocket. "Here you are," he said, putting some coins in Dick's hand.

"Thanks," said Dick, and he put the coins in his pocket.

At the store the pilot telephoned to the field. Then he told Dick where to stand until the bus appeared, and he said good-by and went back to his plane.

By Bus

Soon the big gray bus swept up beside the store and stopped. Dick waited in line and got on with a few other people. He gave his money to the bus driver and walked down the aisle until he found a seat next to the window. When everyone was seated, the bus driver pulled the door shut, and the big bus started down the highway.

The bus went very fast. But every once in a while it stopped to pick up a passenger or to let one off. The bus door would swing open slowly and swing shut slowly. The bus would start up slowly.

Dick began thinking that all this stopping and starting was taking a good deal of time. He hoped his father and mother had got his message and would wait for him.

After a few minutes the bus reached the river and crossed it on a long bridge. Dick could see an oil tanker and some tugboats pulling barges loaded with coal. On another big barge there were several freight cars. It seemed funny for a freight train to be crossing a river on a boat.

In a moment the bus left the bridge and was again traveling swiftly along the highway.

Dick got up and went down the aisle to the bus driver. "I want to get off at the airfield, please," he said.

The driver nodded, never taking his eyes off the highway. "I'll let you know when we get there," he said.

Dick returned to his seat to wait quietly until the driver called him. Pretty soon the bus began to slow down. Was this the airfield? Dick looked out of the window on the other side of the bus. Sure enough, there were the little yellow planes! And now the bus had nearly stopped.

"O. K., sonny," the bus driver was calling to him. "Here's the airfield."

Dick hurried to the front of the bus. Through the wide front window he could see the trailer and the family car with its square-looking fenders. The family had waited for him!

Dick thanked the bus driver and got down. His father was right there to meet him.

"Well, Dick," he said, smiling, "you've done a good deal of traveling already, and your trip has hardly started. What's your favorite way to travel?"

"I'm not sure," Dick answered. "Flying is fun, but I'm glad to come back to the trailer."

R8

Dick hoped Mother wouldn't scold or say, "I told you so," and she didn't. She just asked, "Where did you get money for the bus ride?"

Dick told her. Mr. Dawson handed some coins to Dick. "Run over to the hangar and leave this money there for your pilot," he said.

At the hangar Dick asked about the pilot. He learned that another plane had already gone to help him and both were expected back soon. Now nothing more was wrong, because when Dick got back to the trailer, his father's work on the carburetor was completed, and they were ready to start once more on their journey.

"But for the rest of this day," said Mrs. Dawson, "I want you to ride in the car with us. I just feel as if I'd like to have you where I can see you for a little while."

Dick and his father looked at each other, and Mr. Dawson smiled. So Dick got into the back seat of the car without a word. He knew, and he knew that his father knew, too, that even the best of mothers just can't help being a little too cautious about some things.

Doris Gates

Old Favorites

The Horse with Wings

In a country near to Greece lived a monster called the Chimera. It was part lion, part goat, and part dragon, and completely ugly and terrible. Its breath was fire, and wherever it went the grainfields and houses were burned. It ate cattle and people, so that the very land shook with fear because of this dreadful creature.

The king was anxious to find someone who would kill the monster, but everybody was afraid.

One day a young man arrived at the palace and asked the king for something to do. He was Bellerophon and had been sent by one of his enemies, who hoped he would be killed by the Chimera.

The king told him about the monster and asked him if he would dare to meet and fight the terrible beast.

Bellerophon said, "I am willing to try, but first I must find a wise man who can tell me how to go about this adventure."

He was led to an old wise man who told him, "The best thing you can do is to get the winged horse."

"The winged horse!" cried Bellerophon. "Often have I heard of him. But what man has ever ridden him? He belongs to the gods. Where can I find him?"

"You must go to the temple of Athena at night and sleep there," said the wise man. "It may be that the goddess will appear to you and tell you what you wish to know."

Athena was the goddess of lightning and of storms. It was said that she had tamed the winged horse.

Bellerophon returned to his home in Greece and went at once to the temple of Athena. When night came, he lay down and slept. The goddess appeared to him in a dream and gave him a magic bridle made of gold. When he awoke, the bridle was in his hand.

As Bellerophon gazed at it with wonder, he heard the voice of Athena saying, "Arise and seek the horse. You will find him drinking at the well in the grove near the temple."

With the bridle in his hand, Bellerophon hurried out of the temple and slipped quietly through the grove till he was close to the well. And there stood a beautiful horse, as white as a summer cloud, with silver wings half-folded above his shoulders.

Bellerophon knew that he was looking upon Pegasus, the wonder horse, who could gallop faster than any earthly horse and fly higher than any eagle. But how could he ever hope to ride this creature that belonged to the gods?

198

Suddenly Pegasus lifted his nose and sniffed the air. Then he leaped away, spread his wings, and disappeared into the sky.

Bellerophon's heart sank, but the voice of Athena said, "Wait." So he remained as still as a stone among the trees.

Soon he heard a rush of wings. Softly as a bird, Pegasus dropped down near the well again and began to drink of the sparkling water. So quiet and tame he looked that Bellerophon's hopes rose.

He spoke gently. "Beautiful horse, do not fly away. See, here is your golden bridle, given me by Athena."

Pegasus had lifted his wings to fly, but at sight of the bridle, he stood still and let Bellerophon draw near.

"Help me to kill the monster which is making a whole country unhappy," begged the youth.

The horse looked at Bellerophon for a long moment. Then he took the bit into his mouth and let the youth fasten the bridle.

"Now for the Chimera!" cried Bellerophon leaping upon his back.

At the touch of the magic bridle, Pegasus spread his wings. Up, up he rose, and in a moment Bellerophon was looking down upon the grove and the temple of Athena. Then he was speeding over the mountains and rivers of Greece. Almost before he could draw breath, he saw below him the land blackened by the terrible Chimera.

"How shall I find the monster?" he thought.

The winged horse began to circle slowly toward the earth. Soon Bellerophon could see flames and smoke coming from the mouth of a cave.

With a great shout he drew his sword. Out came the Chimera, hissing and breathing flames from its terrible lion's mouth. Behind that rose the ugly head of a goat, followed by the long snaky body of a dragon. It raised its great claws to attack.

200

As Pegasus swept low above the Chimera, Bellerophon swung his sword. Down it came like lightning and cut off the goat's head. But at once the lion's head and claws rose to the attack more fiercely than ever.

Pegasus paused in the air and gave an angry neigh. Then at a touch of the bridle he rushed once more upon the Chimera. So close he flew that one of the great claws scratched his rider's leg. At the same moment Bellerophon's sword fell, and down sank the lion's head.

Quickly Pegasus whirled about and began to stamp upon the bleeding body of the dragon. It twisted and turned under the pounding hoofs, but at last it lay still. The terrible Chimera was conquered and killed.

Bellerophon rode proudly to the palace, and the king welcomed him as a hero. So grateful were the people of the land that they could not do enough for Bellerophon and the wonderful winged horse. They made ready a great feast, and it was followed by races and games.

Some of the youths who took part in the races wanted to ride Pegasus. But he would let no one but Bellerophon touch him. When others came near, he galloped away or spread his wings and disappeared among the clouds.

Later the king asked Bellerophon to do a great many other hard and dangerous things. So long as he had Pegasus, the youthful hero feared no work, however dangerous it might be. With the help of the winged horse he conquered every enemy. And finally he won the hand of the princess of that country.

A Greek Myth

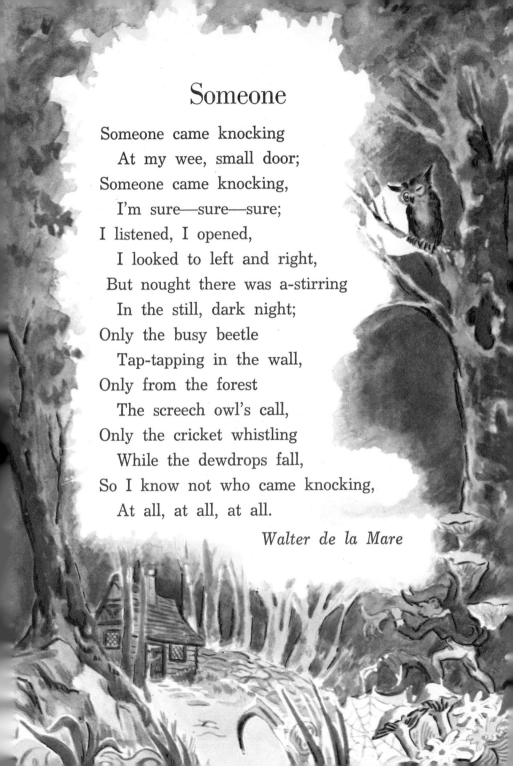

Someone

Someone came knocking
  At my wee, small door;
Someone came knocking,
  I'm sure—sure—sure;
I listened, I opened,
  I looked to left and right,
But nought there was a-stirring
  In the still, dark night;
Only the busy beetle
  Tap-tapping in the wall,
Only from the forest
  The screech owl's call,
Only the cricket whistling
  While the dewdrops fall,
So I know not who came knocking,
  At all, at all, at all.

Walter de la Mare

The Hare and the Tortoise

The Hare was once showing off before the other animals, and he began to boast about his great speed. "I have never yet been beaten," said he, "when I put forth my full speed. I dare anyone here to race with me."

The Tortoise said quietly, "I take your dare."

"Ah, that's a good joke!" said the Hare. "I could run circles round you all the way."

"Keep your boasting till you win," answered the Tortoise. "I took the dare. Now let's race."

So they decided on the racecourse and started. The Hare darted away at once and was out of sight in a moment. But he soon stopped and, to show how little he thought of the Tortoise, he lay down to have a short rest.

The Tortoise crawled steadily on without a pause. When the Hare awoke from sleep, what did he see but the Tortoise right close to the winning line! Though he made his best speed, the Hare could not run up in time to win. With all his boasting and showing off he lost the race.

The Tortoise had won, and he said: "He who is slow and steady wins the race."

An Aesop Fable

The Milkmaid and Her Pail

Betsy, the milkmaid, was on her way to market, carrying the milk in a pail on her head. As she went along, she began to plan what she would do with the money she would get for the milk.

"I'll buy some hens from Farmer Brown," she thought, "and they will lay eggs each morning. The eggs I'll sell to the postman's wife. Then with the money I get from selling the eggs, I'll buy myself a fine new dress with silken sleeves, and a hat trimmed with coral-colored ribbons."

206

So interested did Betsy become in her plans that she began to talk to herself.

"Just wait till I go to market in that new dress and hat! Won't the girls envy me? Polly Pond will almost die of envy. But I'll pretend I don't even see her. I'll just toss my head—"

As she spoke, she tossed her head. The pail fell off and all the milk was spilled.

Betsy went sadly home. There she had to tell her mother how it happened that she had spilled all her milk.

"Ah, my child," said her mother, "never count your chickens before they are hatched."

An Aesop Fable

Hansel and Gretel

Hansel's Clever Plan

Near the edge of a great forest there lived once upon a time a poor woodcutter who had two children: a boy named Hansel and his sister Gretel. They were very poor and once, when there was great need in the land, the man could not even earn their daily bread.

One night, thinking of this, he grew sad at heart. He said to his wife, who was the children's stepmother, not their real mother, "What will become of us? We cannot even feed the children, and there is nothing left for ourselves."

"I know what to do," she said. "Very early tomorrow morning we will take the children into the forest, where it is thickest, and there we will leave them. They will never find the way home, and we shall be done with them."

"No, wife," said the man, "that I will never do. The wild beasts would soon kill them."

"Oh, you stupid one!" said she. "Then we must all four go hungry till we die." And she gave him no peace until he said yes to her plan.

The two children, who also were too hungry to sleep, had heard what their stepmother said to their father. Gretel began to weep and said to her brother, "What is going to happen to us, Hansel?"

"Just be quiet, Gretel," whispered Hansel. "I know how to manage." Then they lay still till their parents were asleep.

As soon as it was quiet, Hansel put on his coat and trousers and slipped outdoors. The moon was shining brightly, and the white pebbles that lay in front of the house shone like pieces of silver. Hansel filled his coat pockets as full as he could with the pebbles.

Then he went back to Gretel and said, "Be comforted, dear little sister, and go to sleep. God will take care of us." Hansel lay down again in his bed and slept soundly.

R8

As soon as the sun rose, the stepmother woke the two children, saying, "Get up, you lazy things, and come with me to gather wood for the fire." Then she gave each of them some bread with no butter and said, "That is for your dinner, and do not eat it before then, for you will get no more."

Gretel put the bread in her small pocket, for Hansel had his pockets full of pebbles. Then they all started off together on their way to the forest.

They had gone but a little way when Hansel stood still and looked back toward the house. This he did again and again, till his father said to him, "Hansel, what are you looking at?"

"Oh, Father," said Hansel, "I am looking at my little white kitten, who is sitting up on the roof. I am sure she is crying for me."

"You silly boy," said his stepmother. "That is not your kitten, but the morning sun shining on the chimney pot."

Of course Hansel had only pretended to be looking at his kitten. He had stayed behind every time to drop a pebble from his pocket.

When they reached the middle of the forest, the children's father told them to gather wood for a fire to keep them warm. So Hansel and Gretel gathered enough wood for a great pile.

When the flames were leaping high, the woman said, "Sit down by the fire, children, and rest. I will go with your father while he cuts wood. When we've finished, we'll come and get you."

So Hansel and Gretel sat by the fire, and at dinner time they ate their pieces of bread. As long as they heard the sounds of the ax, they felt safe, for they believed their father was working near them. But what they heard was only the sound of a bough hanging to an old rotten tree and moving up and down in the wind.

At last, when they had been sitting there a long time, their eyes grew heavy, and they fell fast asleep. When they awoke, it was dark night. The last sparks of the fire were gone.

Gretel began to weep and said, "Oh, how shall we ever get out of the wood?"

But Hansel comforted her, saying, "Let us wait a little while till the moon rises, and then we can easily find the way home."

211

Very soon the full moon rose. Then Hansel took his little sister by the hand and followed the winding path, where the pebbles he had dropped shone like silver in the moonlight.

It was break of day before they came to their father's house and stood knocking at the door. When the wife opened it and saw that it was Hansel and Gretel, she said, "You naughty children, why have you been staying so long in the forest? We thought you were never coming back."

But the father was very happy, for he had been filled with grief to think that he had left them alone in the wood.

212

Lost in the Forest

After some time there was again great need in the land. Again the children heard their stepmother say to their father, "We have not even turnips left to eat. The children must go away. We will take them deeper into the forest this time, and they will not be able to find their way home again. There is nothing else to do."

The man felt heavy at heart, for he thought it was better to share their last bite with the children. But the woman would give him no peace. She continued to scold until, as he had given in before, he had to do so again.

The children were awake and had heard all the talk. So as soon as their parents were asleep, Hansel got up to gather pebbles as he had before. But the stepmother had locked the door and hidden the key, and Hansel could not get out. Still, he told Gretel to forget her grief and go to sleep, for he was sure God would help them.

Early the next morning the stepmother came and pulled the children out of bed. She gave them each a piece of bread, smaller than before.

213

On the way into the forest Hansel broke the bread in his pocket into crumbs, and often stopped to throw a crumb on the ground.

Everything happened just as before. The parents left the children alone in the wood. Gretel shared her bread with Hansel. Then they fell asleep, and the evening came on, and still no one came for them.

When they awoke, it was quite dark, and poor little Gretel was afraid. But Hansel comforted her by saying, "You know, little sister, that we shall easily manage to see our way home by the crumbs of bread that I have left along the way."

But when the moon rose, they could find no crumbs of bread, for the birds of the forest had eaten them. Hansel thought they still might find the way, but they could not.

Although they continued trying all night and all the next day, they could not get out of the wood. They were very hungry, for they had nothing to eat but a few berries they had found.

That night they slept under a tree, and the next morning they tried again to find their way out of the wood.

214

About noon they saw a snow-white bird on the bough of a tree. It sang so sweetly that they stood still to listen. When its song was over, the white bird spread its wings and flew before them. The children followed it and soon saw through a gap in the forest a little house, where the bird stopped and perched on the roof.

To their great surprise, the little house was built of gingerbread and topped with cakes, and its windows were made of sugar.

"Oh," cried Hansel, "this will make a fine feast. I will taste a piece of the roof first. Gretel, you try some of the window."

Hansel on tiptoe reached up and broke off a bit of the roof. Gretel sat by the window and began by tasting a piece of the sugar.

The Wicked Witch

Then the children heard a thin voice call out from inside, "Munch, munch, munch. Who is that munching at my house?"

The children answered, "The wind, the wind, only the wind," and went on eating.

Then the door opened, and a withered old woman came out, leaning on a stick. Hansel and Gretel were so frightened that they let fall what they had in their hands.

The old woman, however, only shook her head and said, "Ah, you dear children, how came you here? Come in and rest after your long journey."

She took them both by the hand and led them into the house. For supper she gave them a wonderful feast of milk and pancakes with honey and applesauce and nuts. Then she showed them two beautiful little beds, and Hansel and Gretel lay down on them and fell fast asleep.

The old woman pretended she was kind, but really she was a wicked witch. She had built a house of gingerbread just to trap hungry children.

Early the next morning, before the children were awake, she got up to look at them. As they lay sleeping so sweetly with smiling faces, she thought, "Ah, what a fine feast they will be!"

Then with her withered hand she pulled Hansel out of bed and led him to a little cage where she shut him in. Although he called and screamed, it was no use.

Then the old witch went back to Gretel and shook her, shouting, "Get up, you naughty thing, and draw some water that I may cook something good for your brother. When he is fat enough, I shall eat him."

Gretel began to weep bitterly, but it was no use. She had to give whatever service the witch wanted. The best of everything was cooked for poor Hansel. Gretel got only clams and vinegar.

Each morning the dreadful old woman went out to the little cage and cried, "Hansel, stick out your finger, that I may feel if you are fat enough for eating."

But Hansel stuck out a little bone, and the withered old witch, who had such weak eyes she was half blind, could not see what it was. Thinking it was Hansel's finger, she wondered why he was not getting fatter. As the weeks passed and Hansel seemed to remain very thin, she decided she could wait no longer.

"Gretel," she said, "go and draw some water. No matter if Hansel be fat or thin, tomorrow I will kill him and cook him."

Oh, how bitterly Gretel cried as she drew the water from the well!

"If we had been eaten by wild beasts in the wood, it would have been better," she thought.

"Stop your squealing," said the wicked witch. "It can do you no good."

218

Early next morning Gretel had to get up, fill the water jugs, and make the fire.

"We will do the baking first," said the old woman. "I have already heated the oven and fixed the dough."

She pushed poor Gretel toward the oven, under which the flames were now leaping brightly.

"Creep in," said the witch, "and see if it is hot enough so that the bread may be baked."

But if Gretel had got in, she would have shut the door upon her and roasted her for dinner.

Gretel guessed this and said, "I don't know how to creep in through that narrow door."

"Stupid goose!" said the witch. "The door is quite large enough. Just look! I could get in myself!" She leaned over and put her head in the oven.

Then Gretel gave her a great push, so that she went in all the way.

Quickly Gretel shut the iron door and fastened it with a heavy bar. Oh, how frightfully the old witch screamed and howled! But Gretel ran straight to Hansel, opened the cage door, and cried, "Hansel, Hansel, we are free! The dreadful old witch is dead!"

Hansel flew out like a bird from its cage, and the children were so happy they ran into each other's arms and danced about.

Treasure

Then, as there was nothing more to be afraid of, they went all over the old witch's house. In a corner they found an old chest full of pearls and sparkling rubies and other precious stones.

"These are better than pebbles," said Hansel, as he filled his pockets. Gretel, too, filled her kerchief with pearls and precious stones.

"Let us go now," said Hansel. "We must find a way out of the witch's wood!"

After they had walked for nearly two hours, they came to a wide stretch of water.

"We cannot get across this," said Hansel. "I see no bridge."

220

"There's no boat either," said Gretel. "But here's a white duck. Let's ask her to help us."

The duck came close to the bank. Hansel got on her back and told his sister to come, too. But Gretel said, "No, that would be hard on the duck. Let's go across one at a time." The duck gave a pleased quack, and that was how they managed.

Then the children went on happily, until they came to a part of the wood they remembered. At last they caught sight of their home. Then they began to run, and rushing into the house, they threw themselves into their father's arms.

The poor woodcutter had not had a peaceful minute since he had left his children alone in the forest. He was full of joy that they were safe, and now they need no longer be afraid, for his wicked wife was dead.

How surprised he was when Gretel shook out her kerchief! Pearls and precious stones fell to the floor! And Hansel took more handfuls of treasure out of his pockets. From that moment all their care was at an end, and they lived together in great joy.

Wilhelm and *Jacob Grimm*

The Stonecutter

Once upon a time there was a stonecutter who worked hard all day long, cutting stones with hammer and chisel. These he made into blocks for building houses and roads. It was hard work, but the stonecutter was contented until one day when he saw the king ride by.

The king was sitting in a fine carriage, and servants held over his royal head a sunshade of turquoise silk with golden tassels.

"Oh," breathed the stonecutter, filled with envy. "If only I were the king, and servants held a silken sunshade over me!"

Now inside the mountain, where the stonecutter was working, lived an old wizard who heard his wish and gave it to him.

In the next moment the stonecutter was himself the king. He was sitting comfortably in the royal carriage. Servants were holding over his head the turquoise sunshade.

"Oh," he breathed happily. "Now I am the greatest of all people alive. I am a monarch. I shall wear a crown. I shall sit on a throne."

But one day when he was about to go on a journey, the servants forgot the sunshade, and the king had to wait in the heat until they brought it. The sun blazed down on his head, and he was very hot and uncomfortable.

"I am not, after all, the greatest thing in the world," he said. "The sun is great enough to make me uncomfortable. Therefore, he is greater than I. Oh, how I wish I were the sun!"

Again the old wizard in the mountain gave him his wish. The stonecutter became the sun. He shone down strongly over the land, burning the grasses and drying up the streams. And the people hid from this burning, blinding sun, and he was happy in his power!

But one day a cloud floated between him and the earth, and he could not shine through it.

"The cloud is greater than the sun," said the stonecutter, who was now the sun. "Oh, if only I could be that cloud!"

The old wizard in the mountain heard his wish, and he at once became the cloud. Now he had the power to send down water upon the earth. And this he did with such might that soon there was a great flood. The river rushed over its banks, carrying with it sheep and calves, donkeys and horses, and even people.

But one thing the flood could not conquer. That one thing was a great rock which stood fast, and the water had to break and go around it.

"What!" cried the stonecutter, who was now the cloud. "Is there something more powerful than I? Oh, if only I could be that rock!"

224

In the next moment the stonecutter became the rock. He held himself proudly and looked far down upon the people moving below him. Rain could not wash him away, and he was contented.

"Now," he said, "I can watch the days and years come and go."

But one day a shaky feeling went all through him. Then he heard a chipping sound. A man was hitting the rock with hammer and chisel, and pieces of the rock were falling upon the ground.

And the stonecutter, who was now the rock, said, "Is there something more powerful than the rock? Oh, if only I could be that man!"

At once the stonecutter became that man and found himself where he had been at the beginning, breaking the rock with hammer and chisel.

"There is nothing greater than man and the work he is best able to do," said the stonecutter. Once more he was contented.

An Oriental Tale

The Steadfast Tin Soldier

Soldier, Dancer, and Goblin

There were once five and twenty tin soldiers. They were brothers, for they had all been made out of the same old tin spoon. They all shouldered their muskets, held themselves upright, and looked straight before them. They were dressed in red-and-blue uniforms and looked very fine.

The first thing they heard, when the lid was taken off the box in which they lay, was the words "Tin soldiers!"

These words were spoken by a little boy, who clapped his hands for joy. The soldiers had been given to him because it was his birthday, and now he was putting them out upon the table.

226

All the soldiers looked so much alike that you couldn't tell them apart—all but one. He had only one leg.

He had been made last of all, and there had not been quite enough tin to make both legs. But he stood as steadfastly upon his one leg as the others did upon their two legs. And it was just this soldier who had some remarkable things happen to him.

On the table where the tin soldiers had been set up were several other toys. The toy that everyone liked best was a pretty little paper castle. Through its tiny windows one could see straight into the hall.

In front of the castle stood little trees around a small looking-glass lake, and on this lake swam little swans made out of wax.

All this was very pretty, but prettiest of all was a little lady who stood at the open door of the castle. She too was cut out of paper, but she wore a dress of the softest silk and a narrow blue ribbon over her shoulders like a scarf. In the middle of the narrow blue scarf was a big tinsel rose.

The little lady stretched out her arms, for she was a dancer. And she lifted one leg so high that the Tin Soldier could not see it. So he thought that, like himself, she had but one leg.

"That would be just the wife for me," thought the Tin Soldier, "if she were not such a great lady. But she lives in a castle, while I have only a box, and there are five and twenty of us in that. It would be no place for a lady. Still, I must try to get to know her."

So he hid behind a carved jewel box on the table. From there he could easily watch the graceful little Dancer in her blue scarf with the big tinsel rose. She still continued to stand on one leg without losing her balance.

When the evening came, all the other tin soldiers were put away in their box, and the people in the house went to bed.

228

Now the toys began to play at visiting and at giving parties. The crayons drew funny pictures. The canary awoke and began to sing. The waxen swans swam about in the looking-glass lake. The tin soldiers rattled in their box, but they could not push the lid off.

The only toys who did not move from their places were the Tin Soldier and the Dancer. She stood on tiptoe with outstretched arms, and he was just as steadfast on his one leg. He never once turned his eyes away from her.

The clock ticked away the hours. Twelve o'clock rang out—and snap! Up flew the top of the carved jewel box. There were no jewels in it, but a little black Goblin. You see, it was really a jack-in-the-box in the shape of a jewel box.

"Tin Soldier," said the Goblin, "keep your eyes to yourself. Look not at what has nothing to do with you!"

But the Tin Soldier pretended he did not hear the Goblin's words.

"Only wait, then, till tomorrow," said the Goblin.

Adventures

Next morning, when the children got up, the Tin Soldier was placed in the window. Maybe it was the Goblin or maybe it was the wind that did it, but somehow the window flew open, and the Soldier fell headfirst to the street below.

Over and over he turned in the air, till at last his cap and the point of his musket stuck fast in the earth between the paving stones, while his one leg stood upright in the air.

The servant girl and the little boy came down to look for him, but they could not find him.

Then it began to rain. Faster and faster fell the drops, until at last it was pouring and the gutters were full of running water. When the rain was over, two boys came by.

230

"Look," said one, "there lies a tin soldier. What a fine red-and-blue uniform! Let us give him a ride in a boat."

So they made a boat out of some old paper, and put the Tin Soldier in the middle of it. Away he sailed down the gutter, while the boys ran along by his side and clapped their hands for joy.

How big the waves were, and how fast the gutter stream ran! The little paper boat rocked up and down, and sometimes whirled round so fast that the Tin Soldier shook. Still he moved not even an eye but looked straight before him and held his musket tightly.

All at once the boat passed into a drainpipe, and it was as dark as his old home in the box with the lid shut down.

"Where am I going now?" thought he. "Yes, to be sure, it is all that Goblin's fault. Ah! if the little lady were but sailing with me in the boat, it might be ever so much darker and I should not care."

Just then a great water rat that lived in the drainpipe darted out suddenly.

"Have you a passport?" asked the rat. "Where is your passport?"

But the Tin Soldier remained silent, and only held his musket tighter than ever.

The boat sailed on, but the rat followed. Oh, how he ground his teeth, and cried out to the bits of sticks and straw, "Stop him! Stop him! He hasn't shown his passport! He hasn't paid the toll."

But the stream grew stronger and stronger. Already the Tin Soldier could see daylight where the drainpipe ended. At the same time he heard a rushing, roaring noise, which might well have frightened a braver man.

232

Think! just where the drainpipe emptied into the river, there was a great waterfall.

Into the waterfall went the boat. The poor Tin Soldier held himself so still that no one might say he moved so much as an eyelid. Three or four times the boat whirled round and round and filled with water to its very edge.

The Tin Soldier stood up to his neck in water. Deeper and deeper sank the boat. Softer and softer grew the paper. He thought of the pretty little Dancer and how he should never see her again.

At last the paper boat parted, and the Tin Soldier fell out. He fell right into the mouth of a great fish!

Oh, how dark it was, darker even than in the drainpipe, and so narrow! But the Tin Soldier kept steadfast. There he lay inside the fish, shouldering his musket as before.

Back and forth swam the fish. It turned and twisted with its shining fins, till at last it lay quite still.

After a time something passed through it like a flash of lightning, and a voice said loudly, "The Tin Soldier!"

Remarkable to tell, the fish had been caught, carried to market, and sold. It had been taken into the kitchen, where it had been cut open with a large knife. That was the lightning flash.

And now the Tin Soldier was being picked out of the fish, and hurried into the room where the family sat. All wanted to see the remarkable man who had traveled about inside of a fish.

He was put on the table, and strange to tell, he was in the very same room as before! He saw the same children, and the same toys stood upon the table. There were the waxen swans, and there was the pretty castle. And the graceful little Dancer still balanced herself upon one leg.

She too was steadfast. That touched the Tin Soldier's heart. He felt like weeping tin tears, but that would not have been acting like a soldier.

He looked at her, and she looked at him, but they said not a word to each other.

And now one of the little boys took the Tin Soldier and flung him into the stove, for no reason at all. It must have been the fault of that Goblin in the jewel box.

The Tin Soldier stood there quite lighted up in the flickering fire. The heat he felt was almost too great to bear. He did not know whether this heat came from the fire or from the feeling in his heart for the pretty little Dancer.

The colors were quite gone from the Soldier's uniform, but whether that was because of his journey in the water or because of grief, no one could say.

He looked at the little Dancer, and she looked at him. He felt that he was melting away, but still he stood steadfast as ever, with his musket on his shoulder.

Then suddenly the door of the room was opened, and the wind caught up the dainty little Dancer. She flew like a fairy straight into the stove to the Tin Soldier. Right away she flashed up brightly in the flickering fire and was gone!

The Tin Soldier melted down into a lump, and the servant girl found him next day, in the shape of a little tin heart. Of the pretty Dancer nothing was left but the tinsel rose, and it was burned as black as a coal.

Hans Christian Andersen

Animals We Like

Pete

Temptation

Boys and dogs understand each other because they are so much alike. They both have many temptations. They often want to do things they know they shouldn't do.

Pete was a dog, an Airedale. He belonged to a boy named Jack. Pete had his temptations. He didn't want to give in to them, and mostly he didn't, but sometimes he did. He always felt bad about it, but he felt bad afterward, because he knew there wasn't any use in trying to feel bad beforehand.

Most of Pete's temptations had something to do with farm life. He had been born on a farm, and he liked the things that belong on a farm. He liked a barn and the animals in a barn. He wanted to hear a pig or two, or watch the cows being milked, and he wanted horses. Jack's family had a barn, but there were no horses in it.

238

Pete knew horses and loved them, and horses were always one of his temptations. When a horse went by, you could see Pete trying not to yield to temptation. He wanted to get up and follow.

Almost always he would just look at the horse and shiver a little, and then turn his head the other way. But once he followed some horses pulling a load of hay. He wasn't discovered till he had gone six or eight miles, and then he had to be brought home.

The biggest temptation Pete ever did yield to came one time when his family went to visit at Jack's grandfather's house in a big town. Of course there were no woods or fields or farm animals, and not even an empty barn. There were only grass and trees around the houses.

Life was very dull for Pete, unless a stray dog came by that he could speak to and pass the time of day with. Most of the time he just lay around in the sun till he got tired of the sun, and then he'd move into the shade till he got tired of the shade. There just wasn't anything interesting anywhere.

One morning a fine team of horses came along
with a load of garden vegetables and a man. The
man stopped the team right in front of Pete. Then
he got out and took the bits out of the horses'
mouths and put on nose bags.

Pete could hardly believe his eyes. Horses?
Yes, real horses! He could smell them. He began
to quiver all over. He got up and went nearer.
The man saw Pete and called in a cheerful voice,
"Hello, Towser!"

Pete didn't mind being called by another name,
for the voice was pleasant. He wagged his tail.

Afterward the man got out a paper bag full of lunch and sat down at the side of the street and began to eat. Pete had had his breakfast and wasn't hungry, but when the man said, "Here, Towser," and offered him something, he took it.

When lunch was over, the man took off the nose bags, climbed to his seat, and said "Giddap!" to the horses and "Good-by, Towser," to Pete.

But the temptation was too great. Pete took one quick look at the house and then hid himself under the wagon, close to the horses' feet, and went along with the team.

R8

Lost

When Jack came out to take Pete for a walk, there was no Pete to be found. Pete didn't come back that day or the next. Jack telephoned the police in the next town. He telephoned the police in another town and in a near-by city. No one knew anything about any kind of stray dog.

Jack's grandfather then called his milkman and found that an Airedale had followed one of the milk wagons. The family was full of joy. They got into the car and drove down to the horse barn. The dog was another Airedale—not Pete.

Everybody inquired everywhere he could think of, face to face and by telephone. By the fourth day it looked as though Pete must be really lost. Jack was worried and uneasy. He wanted to do something, but he didn't know what to do.

Jack's older brother, Lincoln, felt the same way, only he was more grown-up and wouldn't let anyone know. But at last he got out the car and told Jack to come along and they'd go looking for Pete. They were both hoping maybe they'd find Pete by the side of the road somewhere.

242

They traveled up and down highways and back roads in every direction. Lincoln watched one side of the road, and Jack watched the other.

They ran out of gas right in front of their own police station. But they were thinking so much about Pete they didn't stop to find out what the trouble was. Lincoln kept grinding the starter.

A patrolman, just in from his beat, stood in the station doorway and watched and listened and grinned. At last he inquired, "Why don't you take a look at the gas? There's a gas station around the corner."

Lincoln looked. Then he said, "Thanks loads," and walked toward the gas station.

Jack was left with the patrolman. "Haven't seen a stray dog, have you?" he inquired.

The patrolman thought a minute. "Well, now, let me see. What kind of dog was it?"

"An Airedale."

"That's a long-haired dog, isn't it? I don't know dogs very well."

Jack didn't feel like being funny about Pete. He just said shortly, "An Airedale's an Airedale," and turned away.

"Wait a minute, son." When Jack turned back, the patrolman was grinning, and something about the grin made Jack hopeful again.

"Let's go in and see the sergeant. His boy has a dog, and he knows more about dogs than I do."

The sergeant was told the trouble, and he grinned, too. "You say you're looking for a dog?"

"An Airedale."

Jack's hopes went high. He knew that a man who had a boy who had a dog wouldn't be funny about another fellow's lost dog unless he was pretty sure he could help. Jack waited.

"Well, now," the sergeant began very slowly, "three days back we had something in here. He didn't have a brand, and he didn't have a collar, and maybe he was a dog. If he was a dog, just maybe he was an Airedale."

"Sergeant!" Jack shouted.

244

Jack looked as if he might cry any minute. And right then and there the sergeant lost his grin and was gentle and pleasant.

"Hold it, son," he said. "Maybe we can do something." Then he turned to the patrolman, Pat. "Officer, let out the prisoner in cell number thirty and bring him up to us."

"Pete in a cell!" cried Jack.

"Well, now," the sergeant went on, "it's not as bad as it sounds. It's not really a cell. It's a yard where the prisoners take their exercise. The dog's had plenty of food and exercise, and one or another of us has had him out for a run every day. But don't get your hopes up too high. This may not be your dog."

Jack swallowed hard. "I know, sergeant."

"And I've got to be sure he's your dog before I take him off the books. He's lost his collar."

Jack said, "I understand."

The sergeant looked around, then back at Jack. "I tell you. You stand over there behind the door and keep out of sight. You speak up, and if the dog knows your voice . . ." He stopped and asked, "Why didn't you telephone around?"

"We did, sergeant! The whole family has been telephoning in all directions ever since Friday. But we never thought of this station. It's too near."

The sergeant smiled and waved Jack behind the door.

Pat came in leading an Airedale by a chain because he had no collar. The dog walked like an old man. His eyes were dull, and there was no life in him at all.

"Well, prisoner?" the sergeant said in a hard voice. "What have you got to say for yourself?"

The dog looked at the sergeant and gave his tail a weak wag, but he didn't offer to say anything for himself.

The sergeant looked over where Jack was peeping around the edge of the door, with his eyes all shiny and excited.

Jack drew back and said, "It's Pete, all right!"

Pete's head came up like a shot, and his ears quivered, and his tail came alive. He looked around like a fellow looking for his stocking on Christmas morning. Then he gave a bound that pulled the chain out of Pat's hand, and a bark that nearly took the roof off. He was over behind the door in a second, eating Jack up between barks.

The sergeant grinned at Pat. "Yes, I guess maybe it's the boy's dog all right, officer."

The sergeant told Jack to keep the chain if he was planning to take that wild animal into the traffic. Somehow Jack got Pete out of the police station, found his brother Lincoln, and pushed Pete into the car.

Pete barked halfway back to the house, and when he wasn't barking, he was whimpering. And when he wasn't whimpering, he was crying like a baby. If ever a dog was telling a man how sorry he was and how ashamed, and promising never to follow another cart again or even to look cross-eyed at another horse, it was Pete.

He promised right then and there never to yield to that temptation again. And he never did.

Tom Robinson

Flipper

Once there was a baby named Flipper. This baby could not walk, because she had no feet. She had no hands either. Flipper was a baby sea lion. Instead of having hands and feet, or paws or claws, she had four wide, flat flippers. That's how she got her name.

These four little flat flippers were useless right now. Baby Flipper, new, tiny, and helpless, lay on a large sunny rock. Her furry skin was gray-brown in color. Flipper drank milk from her mother, as many baby land animals do, and her mother took care of her. So she had nothing to do all day but lie on her stomach on a rock in the sun.

This rock was on Cliff Island in the Pacific Ocean. There were big brown rocks all about, some high as a house, some low and washed by waves. There were short stretches of white sand, broken in places by gray-green beach grass that moved in every breeze. Out beyond was the water, blue-green in the wind, golden in the sun, and almost black under the clouds.

When Flipper grew tired, she closed her eyes and went to sleep, with her chin on the rocks like a puppy.

She went to sleep with the roaring and barking and squealing of all her family around her. And it was not a little family of five or ten or even twenty, but a family of about two hundred sea lions. They all lived together, played together, and ate together. They all talked at once, and sometimes they fought with one another.

The mothers, swimming and looking for food, would moo to their babies. One of the great father sea lions guarded them. He would sit on a big rock, turning his head—watching, watching. When he saw any danger near, he would shout, "Hook! Hook!" in loud, warning barks. This would bring all the sea lions racing back to land.

Flipper liked to hear the great barks of the old sea lion on guard.

250

There were other sounds too. There was the crying of the sea birds as they wheeled above the rocks. There was the soft splash of the waves like a lullaby. Sometimes it grew to a roar when the wind came up and sent dark clouds racing across the sky.

Best of all, Flipper liked the sound of her own mother's voice as she came swimming home. Her mother was a beautiful, dark-brown sea lion with gentle ways.

When Mother Brownie was going out into the deep water to get food, she would rub her nose against Flipper's nose and say softly, "Ah-h-h-h-h, ah-h-h." When she came home, tired and full of dinner, she was so happy to see her baby she would sniff her and feel her with her face and her flippers and say gently, "Mooo! Mooo!"

To this, Flipper would answer, "Maaah! Maaah!" because she was so glad to have her mother at home again.

As Flipper grew a little bigger, she began to move about on her stomach. Often, when her mother went out to fish, she played with her friend Squealer.

Squealer was a fat little sea lion who cried almost all the time. Squealer's mother, Rowdy, wasn't around very much. She saw that Squealer had enough to eat so that he didn't go hungry. And she left him where he couldn't fall into the sea, but that was about all she did for him.

Even when Squealer's mother was with him, he didn't seem very happy. His mother barked at him when he cried, and shook him when he was clumsy.

Since Mother Rowdy was so careless and rough with her baby, it was often Flipper's mother, Brownie, who saw that Squealer was safe and warm.

Even Flipper tried to take care of Squealer, although they were the same age. She snuggled near him to keep him warm. She played with him, rolling over and nipping him in fun. And sometimes she fought with him, too.

One of their fights took the baby sea lions into danger. Late one afternoon Mother Brownie went swimming off to eat. Squealer was hungry and cold, for his mother had been gone all day, and he kept pushing against Flipper to keep warm. Sleepily Flipper edged away from him, until suddenly she went rolling down off her smooth rock to a ledge below.

Luckily it was a drop of only a few inches. Flipper was safe, but she had bumped her chin on a sharp stone and was wide awake and angry. So she set up a squealing and barking that made the old sea lion on guard turn his head.

Squealer felt very cold when Flipper left so suddenly, and his only thought was to get close to her again. So he hopped along on his flippers and slid down beside her. Then, to his surprise, she turned on him with her sharp baby teeth and nipped his neck!

Squealer hadn't meant to hurt Flipper, and so this made him very angry. Then the baby sea lions fought each other with their teeth and their flippers. They squealed as they rolled over and over and bit at each other.

Mother Brownie saw them as she came swimming slowly home at dusk.

She lifted her smooth, sharp nose out of the water and called "Hook! Hook!" to tell them to stop. But Flipper and Squealer could not hear her over their own noise.

The tide was high. Brownie could see the babies rolling closer and closer to the edge of the ledge. They could not swim yet, and she knew that she could not save two of them!

She wanted to get there as fast as possible. So instead of landing on the lowest rocks and jumping up step by step as she did most of the time, she gathered her smooth brown body for a great leap.

Pushing against the water with her strong flippers, Mother Brownie made a high, graceful leap. It took her sliding gently and surely between the two angry little sea lions.

Flipper and Squealer were so surprised to see her leap home, flying almost like a bird, that they both stopped fighting at once.

Mother Brownie shook her smooth head at them both. Then she rubbed noses with them and scolded, "Ah-h-h-h! Ah-h-h-h!" in her kind and gentle voice.

Flipper was already drinking her milk when Squealer's mother, Rowdy, appeared. She came hopping up the rocks just in time to feed her son before it got dark.

Then all the sea lions snuggled as close together as possible and went to sleep. The sky grew darker and darker. The stars came out far above them, and the sea beyond the rocks grew blacker and blacker. There was only the splashing of the waves and the feel of the cold, salty night wind, blowing across the Pacific.

Irma S. Black

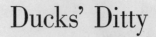

Ducks' Ditty

All along the backwater,
Through the rushes tall,
Ducks are a-dabbling,
Up tails all!

Ducks' tails, drakes' tails,
Yellow feet a-quiver,
Yellow bills all out of sight
Busy in the river!

Slushy green undergrowth
Where the roach swim—
Here we keep our larder,
Cool and full and dim.

Everyone for what he likes!
We like to be
Heads down, tails up,
Dabbling free!

High in the blue above
Swifts whirl and call—
We are down a-dabbling
Up tails all!

Kenneth Grahame

Australia's Teddy Bears

You may have to think back several years to remember the time when you cared about Teddy bears. But suppose one day you were walking under some trees. And suppose you looked up and saw a live Teddy bear hanging on to a branch of one of those trees and looking down at you. Should you care about Teddy bears then?

I think you would. And it could happen to you if you should ever visit Koala Park in Australia, far across the Pacific Ocean.

This park gets its name from the strange little animals that live in it. These strange little animals look just like the Teddy bears you used to play with. They are called koalas.

The koala has a round body about two feet long, covered with silky gray fur. It weighs about twelve pounds. Furry ears stand out on each side of its friendly face, and it has bright black eyes set close to a nose which is like a patch of black cloth.

The baby koala rides about in its mother's pocket until it is five months old. Then it comes out for a look at the world. From then until it is a year old, it rides on its mother's back.

The koala likes to live in trees. It comes down out of one tree only when it wants to climb into another tree. The food of the koala is leaves— the leaves of gum trees. And if it cannot get leaves of special kinds of gum trees, it will go hungry and thirsty. It does not even drink water.

Of the several hundred kinds of gum trees, there are only about six kinds whose leaves the koala will eat. You can see that the koala is a hard animal to raise, because it eats only this special kind of food. Koalas that have been taken away from Australia to zoos in other countries have not lived very long.

Even in their own country the koalas have had many hard times. Hunters killed off almost all of them to get their fur. If it had not been for a few people who loved them, there might not be any koalas at all today. As it is, there are only a small number of them alive, and most of these are in special places set aside for them.

One such place is an island. During the Second World War, when the people of Australia had more things to worry about than koalas, a visitor once went out to the island and found that the koalas had nothing to eat. All the leaves were gone from the gum trees, and the poor little animals were nearly dead.

Even though the people in the near-by city were busy helping to win the World War, they took pity on the koalas. Though they had very little gasoline for travel, they gathered leaves from the gum trees around their own houses and took them to the island. There they tied the leaves to the empty branches for the koalas to eat.

There are now laws in Australia to protect the koalas. So we may hope that there will be many more of the strange little animals.

The people of Australia have a pet name for the koala. It is Joey.

Those of you who keep postage stamps will be interested to know that Australia has put a picture of the little Joeys on a postage stamp. Only very important people get their pictures on a country's postage stamps.

We have a likeness of one of our American animals on one of our coins. It is a bison, or buffalo. Like the koalas, the bison were almost all killed off before anyone thought of a law to protect them. Now many bison live safely in the great parks of the West.

And now the little koala will always be free from danger in Australia. He has earned this good care because he is so tame and friendly. He will climb down out of his tree into your arms almost any time, put his furry little paws around your neck, or snuggle close against your shoulder like a purring kitten. Who wouldn't care about a Teddy bear like that?

Doris Gates

Tinker of the Big Top

One More Chance

Tinker was a circus monkey. He had not been with the circus very long. Often he sat huddled up on the perch in his cage. Except for his bright brown eyes, which were like shiny buttons, and his long curled-up tail, the little monkey looked like a soft ball of brown fur.

As he sat huddled up on his perch, he wished that he could swing in a tree again, the way he used to in his treetop home in the green jungles of South America.

The other monkeys all had something to do in the circus. Some rode in the pony races, and others played with the clowns. Tinker did not know that it was just because he was new that he was being left in his cage.

As the circus traveled from town to town, Tinker slowly grew used to the bright lights and all the people around his cage. He learned that the boys and girls liked to see him swing by his tail.

The children would laugh when he jumped up and down on his perch and clapped his hands as they did. But still, Tinker was not happy.

One afternoon while Tinker was doing tricks for the children, Dan Field, the head animal man, stood watching him closely. Later Dan called Toto, the best clown, over to Tinker's cage.

"Toto," said Dan, "I think Tinker is ready to go into the show now. You take him out tomorrow and try him in the pony races."

The next day Toto put Tinker on one of the ponies and led the pony around the ring. As long as Toto held on to Tinker's belt, the monkey was quiet. But as soon as Toto took his hand off the belt, Tinker began to cry.

Every day for two weeks Toto tried to teach Tinker to ride the pony. But it was no use. Tinker was always afraid. At last Toto went to Dan Field and said, "It's no use. That monkey just can't learn to ride."

"How about trying him in the clown act?" Dan asked.

Toto tried earnestly to teach Tinker to tumble and dance as the other monkeys in the clown act did. But try as he would, he could not get Tinker to learn.

So Toto went to Dan again and said, "It's no use. That monkey is too dull to learn anything. I don't believe he'll ever be a show monkey."

"I'll tell you," said Dan. "Take Tinker into the Big Top this afternoon at show time and try him out there."

That afternoon Toto put a little green suit on Tinker and took him to the Big Top at show time. He put Tinker on a perch just inside the tent and fastened his belt to a post. "Well, old fellow," said Toto, "this is your last chance."

Then the drums rolled long and loud and the music began. Tinker looked toward the middle ring. There two handsome men and a pretty lady were bowing this way and that, while everyone clapped and shouted, "The Flying Rogers! The Flying Rogers!"

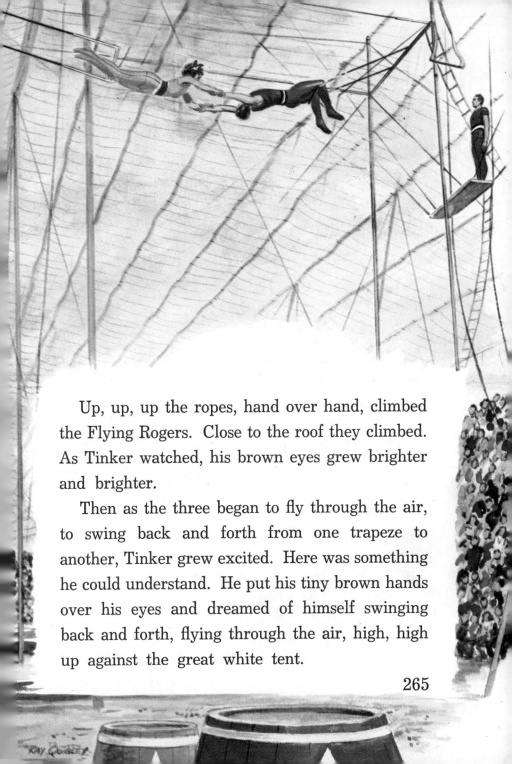

Up, up, up the ropes, hand over hand, climbed the Flying Rogers. Close to the roof they climbed. As Tinker watched, his brown eyes grew brighter and brighter.

Then as the three began to fly through the air, to swing back and forth from one trapeze to another, Tinker grew excited. Here was something he could understand. He put his tiny brown hands over his eyes and dreamed of himself swinging back and forth, flying through the air, high, high up against the great white tent.

When it was time for Tinker to go into the ring with the clowns, he hardly knew what was happening. Suddenly he saw that he was out in front of a whole tent full of people. There was noise and music. Everyone laughed and clapped. He felt strange and lost down on the ground. He looked this way and that. He saw Toto.

Straight for the clown's legs he flew. Quickly he climbed to Toto's shoulder. He was whimpering like a child.

How glad he was to be put back in his own cage! Toto and Dan were standing near by, and Toto said, "There's no use working with him. He'll never be a show monkey."

"I guess you're right," said the animal man, "but I can't understand it. He acts bright enough." Then he added, "We'll just have to keep him in the animal tent until we can trade him off."

For a while Tinker sat and dreamed about those wonderful swings way up in the top of the tent. If only he could get up there and swing! Now and then he tried the door to his cage, hoping to find it unlocked, but it never was.

266

Tinker's Act

A few days later Tinker sat huddled on his perch, feeling very unhappy. Would he never get a chance to swing on the trapeze? He would have been more unhappy if he had understood just what Dan and Toto were saying as they stood near his cage.

"We'll let Tinker go in this lot," Dan said. "The man has a fine brown bear cub he wants to trade off for a monkey and two ponies."

"Yes, we might as well," answered Toto. "We can't teach him anything."

That evening Tinker decided to work his way through the bars of his cage. He wiggled and wiggled. His leg and shoulder hurt, but he did not care. He was in earnest and he would not give up. At last he got through and dropped to the ground. He kept in the shadows as he quickly ran toward the Big Top.

All the seats were empty and waiting. The ropes and wires hung from the roof of the great tent. Everything was ready for the next show. In another hour the tent would be filled.

But now Tinker had the whole place to himself. He darted across the tent to the middle ring and to the ropes that held the trapezes high in the air. Then, in a flash, he sped up the ropes, until he found himself on a small platform close to the roof.

He reached out a small hairy hand and clasped the nearest trapeze. He chattered softly to himself. From trapeze to trapeze he flew. Afterward he sat and dreamed happily until time for the show to begin.

Tinker awoke with a start when the bright lights came on. He jumped from the tiny platform to a trapeze. The drums rolled loudly and the music began. Tinker's heart sang as he sat watching. The grand parade started around the great tent. The show was on.

A while later the lights began to go down. Then they went off, only to come on full again.

Tinker's heart was beating fast.

268

The Flying Rogers were bowing and smiling handsomely in the middle ring. Then they were high in the air, ready for their act.

One of the men stood on the tiny platform. But as he reached for the trapeze, it went swinging out with a small brown monkey hanging to it. The pretty lady gave a sharp little cry.

Soon all the people, even the Flying Rogers, were watching Tinker closely. Never before had they seen such trapeze tricks. Tinker went swinging back and forth, back and forth. He twisted and turned in the air. He hung by one hand, then by one toe, then by his tail.

269

The children jumped up and down and clapped and shouted. Everyone held his breath, afraid that any minute the tiny monkey would come falling to the ground. But Tinker had learned tricks in his happy jungle days that even the Flying Rogers had never thought of. He went on, swinging back and forth, from one trapeze to another, never missing once.

No one knows how long Tinker would have gone on flying and swinging up there. He was having a wonderful time, and so were the watching people. But after a while the pretty lady caught the rope and took Tinker into her arms.

"Bow, Tinker, bow!" she whispered to him, as she put him down beside her on the platform.

Tinker jumped up and down and clapped his hairy little hands together.

A great roar filled the Big Top as everyone clapped and clapped and clapped. The children shouted, "More, more, more!" and the roar grew. Then as Tinker was lowered to the middle ring by a rope, the boys and girls, and the grownups too, stood up and cheered and cheered.

Toto stood close to the rope. He held out his arms, and Tinker jumped into them. At the door of the Big Top, Dan Field stood waiting for Toto. He had heard the cheers and the clapping and had come to see what it was all about.

As Toto came out carrying Tinker, Dan called to him, "Well, this is a fine how-de-do! It's a good thing that buyer is here waiting for this runaway. Send him right off!"

"Wait," said the clown. "Didn't you hear how hard the people clapped?"

271

"Yes, and how they laughed and shouted?" asked the ringmaster, who had hurried out, too.

"We can't throw away an act like that," said Toto. "It's a special."

"The children loved it," added the ringmaster.

"Hmm, well!" Dan Field said gruffly.

"Why, Tinker stopped the show!" said Toto.

"He surely did," put in the ringmaster.

"Well, I suppose . . ." said Dan.

"Then it's all set," said Toto happily.

"TINKER, THE ONLY MONKEY TRAPEZE STAR IN THE WORLD! How does that sound?" asked the ringmaster.

Tinker chattered away happily. He did not know whether he had been good or naughty. He clasped his hands together and looked at Toto with shining, bright eyes.

The clown said, "It's all right, Tinker, old fellow. You're a show monkey after all."

From that day on, a very happy and clever monkey called Tinker did a special flying-trapeze act for his friends the children. And from that day on, he was never homesick.

Esther Van Sciver

Little Vic

A Queer Race Horse

Little Vic's father and mother were both race horses, and so everyone expected that little Vic would be one, too. He looked just like his famous father, even to the white star on his wide forehead. But even if he looked like a race horse, Little Vic didn't act like one. He was much too gentle to suit his trainer.

"I like to see a colt with more fight in him," the trainer would say when Little Vic came back to the stables after a workout. "His father was hard to work with, but nothing seems to trouble Little Vic."

"Little Vic's O.K.," the stable boy would say. "He's got more sense than all the other horses put together. Just you wait until he gets on the track. He'll show them a thing or two."

The stable boy loved Little Vic and believed in him.

The day came at last for Little Vic's first real race. The stable boy rubbed him until his coat was shiny even in the shadows. Little Vic nibbled him playfully on the shoulder as if to say, "Take it easy, boy. It's not so important as all that."

Everyone was much excited when Little Vic came dancing out on to the track.

"He looks just like his father," they said. "He's the best looking colt of the bunch."

The horses lined up at the starting gate. Several of the colts were frisky and backed and jumped. Little Vic, however, stood very still and waited for the others to quiet down.

274

At last the barrier was lifted, and a shout went up from the crowd, "They're off!"

And so they were—all but Little Vic. He still stood quietly. But his head was lifted to where a silver airplane flew low over the track. He had never seen one before.

His rider did everything he could to make him start. He even hit him with his whip. Little Vic just went on watching the airplane, and the race was run without him.

The stable boy still believed in him, however.

"It was his first race," he said to the trainer. "He'll start all right the next time."

The next day Little Vic was again put into the race. Again he stood with the other horses at the starting gate. Again he stood quietly. But this time his rider was ready for him. As soon as the barrier was lifted, he laid his stinging whip sharply across Little Vic's sides.

Now Little Vic had sense enough to know that he had done nothing for which to get a whipping. It made him very angry. All the fire and life of his famous father came up in him. He forgot all about the race and everything else except throwing the mean rider off his back.

With a snort he whirled about and began to buck. He bucked as hard as a wild colt. He bucked so hard that his rider went sailing off into the air.

Back at the stable, his friend the stable boy said, "You were right to throw that rider. He isn't good enough to ride a horse like you."

Little Vic nibbled his feed and seemed very happy now about everything. But his owner was far from happy. Two times now Little Vic had not started in a race. That meant that he was no good as a race horse. The owner decided to sell him.

A man from Arizona who had seen the race that day was willing to give a fair price for Little Vic. So the next day the stable boy said good-by to him, and Little Vic was shipped to Arizona.

The man who bought him was named Mr. George, and he lived on a huge cattle ranch. It was so big that a great cross-country highway ran right through it.

In many places this highway crossed small river beds. Most of the year these Arizona river beds were dry. But at times they were filled with water from storms in the mountains. The water rushed down so fast that sometimes people got caught in the path of it and were drowned. These sudden rivers are called flash floods.

Racing for a Reason

One evening Mr. George was riding Little Vic along the edge of one of the deep, dry river beds.

Little Vic had become the favorite horse at the ranch. All the cowboys liked him. Mr. George rode no other horse. He didn't care that Little Vic could not run so fast as his famous father. He was sure and safe.

After a while they came to a car parked at the edge of the river bed. Down below, a party of tourists was gathered around a campfire.

"Hi, there," Mr. George called down to them. "You aren't planning to camp there tonight, are you?"

"Oh, yes," they called back. "We're out of the wind down here."

"But it isn't safe," said Mr. George. "A mountain storm might send a flood along here before morning. You'd be caught and drowned."

The tourists laughed. "You're just trying to scare us because we're new to this country."

"You could camp in the old adobe house you passed two miles back," Mr. George said, but the tourists did not move. At last he rode away and left them there. "It may not rain after all," he thought.

But he had ridden about two miles beyond the camp, when Little Vic stopped suddenly with a snort. His sharp ears had caught a sound, and his nose had sniffed something new. Mr. George wondered what could have frightened his horse, and he smiled at Little Vic's pointing ears. It was likely just a coyote!

Then suddenly he too heard something. He heard the sound of rushing water. What he feared had happened. There had been a storm in the mountains, and now the flood was rushing down the dry river bed.

The tourists would not hear it in time to climb up to safety. They would all be drowned!

279

He and Little Vic must try to get to them
ahead of the water. He turned the horse sharply
and bent low in the saddle.

Little Vic jumped forward just as a race horse
should when the barrier is lifted before him. Then
he went into his racing stride. No, not his stride
after all. It was his father's stride, famous the
world over for its might and speed.

Above the roar of the water, Mr. George could
hear the mighty pounding of Little Vic's hoofs.
It was like the beat of music to his ears.

On and on went the horse, but on and on came
the water. Its roar seemed louder now. Was this
because the horse was tiring, and his stride was
getting slower?

Mr. George looked back, but in the dark he
could see nothing. Once Little Vic hit a stone,
and sparks shot out into the night. But still his
long legs worked smoothly and swiftly.

And now, ahead of them, Mr. George could see
a small light shining. He knew it was the campfire
of the tourists. He said something to Little Vic
and saw one of the horse's ears turn back to
catch the words.

It seemed then that Little Vic flew through the night, so fast did he go, his hoofs hardly touching the earth. The wind whistled past Mr. George's ears. He knew that never in all the long story of racing had any horse ever turned in a better race than this. Little Vic's father could be proud of him after all.

At last they were close enough so that the pounding of horses' hoofs reached the ears of the tourists. Mr. George shouted. The people quickly climbed up the steep bank out of the river bed. By the time Little Vic tore past them, the last one had reached safety.

Now they could hear the roar of the water. In another minute it rushed past them, washing out the campfire and taking all the camping things along with it. But the tourists didn't care. Because of Little Vic, they were safe and sound. They were also very, very thankful.

They crowded around the horse and his rider. But Little Vic wouldn't let them touch him. Like every winner after a race, he felt all on edge. He lifted his head proudly and looked out into the darkness. Mr. George reached down and smoothed his mane and his lovely neck.

"You're not a horse," he said, "you're a wonder! You could be a race horse all right. But you've got too much sense for that. You run your best only when there's a good reason for it. And you'll never have a better reason than you had tonight."

Little Vic lowered his head and reached around to nip playfully at Mr. George's boot. It seemed as if he could understand every word and, like all real heroes, wanted to turn attention away from himself.

Doris Gates

They Earned Their Way

The Seventh Pup

Not Wanted

In some ways Billy Bent was a very lucky boy, and he knew it. But in other ways he wasn't very lucky.

In the first place Billy loved dogs. He had already decided that when he grew up he was going to earn his living by training them. That wouldn't happen for quite a while, though, because Billy was only nine years old. But already he had a way with dogs and an eye for them, too.

Anyway, that's what his neighbor Mr. Riggs said, and he should have known, for he raised Boston terriers, which people for miles around came to buy.

The people Billy lived with next door were paid by the city to take care of him, because he had no family. That was not lucky, but living next door to Mr. Riggs was lucky.

Now one day Queenie, the best dog Mr. Riggs owned, had a litter of puppies. Billy happened to be right there when Mr. Riggs found Queenie's new family.

284

"Well, old lady," Mr. Riggs said gently, and Queenie looked at him with clear, unafraid eyes. "How many babies have you this time?"

He moved Queenie out of her box, and there, huddled together, were seven black-and-white puppies. Mr. Riggs was delighted to see so many, for Queenie was one of the very best Boston terriers in the world. People who came to buy a dog always wanted one of her puppies.

All these new puppies had strong bodies and perfect markings. All but one! His markings were anything but perfect. His white shirt front came too far around his shoulders like a shawl. One half of his face was black and the other, white. On the white side he had a black ear, and on the black side, a white ear.

He couldn't have looked more sadly mixed up and awkward. But saddest of all was his tail. It was two times as long as it should have been.

285

"Well," said Mr. Riggs, "it won't be hard to decide what to do with that seventh pup." He had put the six good puppies in the box, and the seventh was lying all by himself on the floor of Queenie's pen.

"What do you mean?" asked Billy. But in his heart he knew what Mr. Riggs was going to say.

"Queenie won't have milk for more than six puppies, and that seventh one isn't any good anyway. I'll just have to kill him."

Billy looked at the seventh pup, and all at once he knew that he loved him better than all the rest of Queenie's litter put together. Perhaps it was because the puppy wasn't wanted that Billy loved him so.

Billy knew that feeling of not being wanted, because nobody cared much about him, either. He always had enough to eat and a good bed to sleep in, but just the same he knew what it meant not to be wanted.

Perhaps the puppy felt the same way. So now Billy wanted that awkward, homely seventh pup. He wanted him more than anything in all the world.

286

"Yes, I'll have to kill him," Mr. Riggs said. "But he's so homely, it won't matter much."

Then Billy spoke. "Don't kill him," he begged. "Give him to me."

Mr. Riggs looked at Billy in surprise. "He's too little to take away from his mother," he said. "You couldn't feed him, boy."

"Yes, I could," Billy said eagerly. "I'll feed him with a baby's bottle. And if he doesn't keep well and strong—why then I'll give him up."

Mr. Riggs could think of nothing to say against Billy's plan, and so he gave him the pup. Billy lifted it from the floor while Mr. Riggs held on to Queenie. Then Mr. Riggs gave Billy one of the baby bottles which he kept at the kennel, and Billy went proudly home with the seventh pup held close in his arms. This was his first dog.

The man the city paid for keeping Billy was sitting on the front porch drinking lemonade when Billy reached the house.

"Where on earth did you find that?" he scolded when he saw the pup.

This was the moment Billy had been waiting for. "How do you like my dog?" he asked.

287

"What do you mean by 'my dog'?" The man's voice was sharp.

"Mr. Riggs just gave him to me for keeps."

"Well, you can take him right back," said the man. "What made you think you could have a dog? Besides, he's about the homeliest thing I ever had to look at."

"I'll keep him under the back porch," begged Billy. "I'll feed him and exercise him, and he won't be in anybody's way."

"Oh, yes?" said the man. "And who'll pay for his food? You eat more than I get for your keep. There isn't even a bone for a dog to gnaw."

Billy swallowed hard. "He's not a very big dog," he said. "He wouldn't eat much, and I'll give him some of what's coming to me."

"That's easy to say," said the man. "You take him right back to Mr. Riggs."

288

A Job for Billy

Billy had to obey. He walked sadly back to the Riggs place with the pup. But Mr. Riggs wouldn't take him back.

"He's your dog," he told Billy, who was trying to rub the tears off his face. "When I give a dog, I give him for good."

"But he"—Billy nodded toward the house next door—"he won't let me keep him. He won't let me have the food for him, and I couldn't let the puppy go hungry."

"I haven't said he would go hungry," said Mr. Riggs. "I only said he was still your dog. How about having him board and room over here?"

"I haven't any money to pay for his keep," said Billy, without any hope.

"I haven't asked for money," said Mr. Riggs, and smiled. "I thought maybe you'd like to earn the pup's keep."

Billy gave a huge sniff and looked with surprised eyes at Mr. Riggs.

"How?" he asked.

"I've seen for some time that you have a way with dogs," Mr. Riggs said. "I'll need a little help now and then, specially now that this new litter has arrived. Suppose you come over whenever you get the chance and mix feed and clean kennels, and I'll board the pup for your pay."

Billy's face broke into a smile so bright that Mr. Riggs couldn't face it and had to look down at the ground for a minute. Billy could hardly believe what he'd heard. Work for the pup's board! Why, he'd rather be working around dogs than doing anything else in the world.

"Whee, Mr. Riggs," he said in a long happy breath. "Whee! Thanks."

The puppy wiggled and tried to wag its tail. Mr. Riggs laughed. "His tail isn't too long to wag, even if it is too long for a terrier."

Soon Billy and Mr. Riggs began calling the seventh pup Too-long because of his too-long tail.

The weeks passed and then the months. Too-long grew, and his tail grew with him.

From the first he got along wonderfully on Billy's care. Most likely that was because there was so much love mixed up in it.

290

After all, it turned out to be a lucky thing that the people Billy lived with didn't care much about him. If they had, they might not have wanted him to spend so much time away from home.

As it was, Billy spent more time at the Riggs place than he did at his own. As soon as school was over, he ran next door, where Too-long fell upon him with sharp barks of welcome.

Billy was careful not to spoil him. And whenever he had a chance, he worked with the pup, teaching him the things a well-trained dog should know. By the time Too-long was six months old, he had learned to follow close at Billy's heels, to get down when told to do so, and to bring a ball right to his master's feet. He obeyed each command so eagerly that teaching him was fun.

Even Mr. Riggs said that Too-long, for all his bad looks, was as sharp as a needle. By the time he was a year old and Billy was ten, Too-long stayed exactly where he was told to stay, jumped over a stick to bring the ball, spoke, shook hands, and rolled over. Billy thought he was the most wonderful dog in the world.

· "You've done a good job with him," Mr. Riggs said. "You like him so much, I was afraid you'd spoil him. It's too bad he can't ever go into the show ring. He could be a winner with what he knows if he just had looks to go along with it."

The Dog Show

Then, one day just a week before the dog show, bad luck decided to pay a visit to Mr. Riggs. The only dog he had planned to enter in the show that year was taken with a bad cold. Mr. Riggs's face looked as long as Too-long's tail.

Billy, seeing how sad Mr. Riggs looked, began to put his mind to work. He knew a thing or two about dog shows. That very day, with Too-long at his heels, he went downtown to the dog-show office.

He didn't say a word about it to Mr. Riggs, but the evening before the show day he bathed and brushed Too-long carefully. Then he and the dog went over all the things Too-long had learned.

The next morning Billy borrowed a collar and a rope from the kennel office. With Too-long at his heels he started for the dog show, still without saying a word of his plan to anyone.

Two hours later Mr. Riggs, walking about among the barking dogs and crowding people, came at last to the ring where the obedience trials were being held. A large crowd was gathered there, and at first he could not see what was going on. When at last he got a good look, his mouth opened wide in surprise.

There, going through his tricks as easily and perfectly as he did in his own back yard, was Too-long. And with him was Billy, the boy nobody cared very much about.

Near the ring were other dogs, held a little to one side by their masters while Too-long was having his turn. There were all kinds of dogs, big and little, fine and homely, but the homeliest of them all was Too-long.

Mr. Riggs remembered then that there is one part of every dog show where looks don't count. That is the obedience trials. If a dog has had the right training and does exactly what his master commands him to do, nobody cares what he looks like. And if he obeys perfectly enough, he can even win the blue ribbon.

Mr. Riggs felt his eyes grow wet as he watched the little dog, with his tail held out straight and long behind him. There was such an eagerness in the way he tried to obey Billy's commands that it seemed as if he knew he was the only dog from his kennel who had a chance of bringing home a prize ribbon that day.

And Billy was as eager as the dog. His face was red and anxious, and he never once looked at the crowd.

294

He didn't even seem to hear the clapping when Too-long jumped the low bars and brought him the make-believe bone. He was so busy trying to send a thought message to Too-long that the bars were no more than the stick at home.

Too-long did everything Billy told him to. And with every act well done, his eyes shone with joy, as if he were saying thanks to the people for watching him. The homely little dog had won the hearts of the people, as had the boy with the eager face and the patched trousers.

At last it was over, and after a while a man came up to Billy and handed him a white ribbon. Too-long had won fourth place in the obedience trials. The man said it might be a first next year when Billy had learned more about training dogs for the trials.

Mr. Riggs caught up with Billy outside. "I saw you in there," he said. "I was proud of you."

Billy held out the white ribbon that Too-long
had just won. "You can put it in the glass box
with the others," he said. "The kennel will have
a ribbon to show for this year after all."

Mr. Riggs took the ribbon. "Thank you, Billy,"
he said. "I'm very happy about what you've
done for the kennel. And there's another thing.
I think after what happened today that Too-long
has earned his own keep. How would it seem to
work for real money instead of for his board?"

"For you?" asked Billy, a light coming into
his face.

"For me," said Mr. Riggs, "outside school hours,
of course."

"Whee!" said Billy. "I'd like it a lot."

"Then you're to be my right-hand man," said
Mr. Riggs, and rested his hand on Billy's shoulder.
Under it he could feel Billy pull his shoulders
up very straight.

Doris Gates

Diego Wins

A Young Potter

Diego lives in Cuba. Most of the people in Cuba, even boys like Diego, work in the sugar fields, for much sugar cane is raised there. Cuba also raises other things, such as coffee, bananas, pineapples, and beans for making chocolate.

One day Diego was on his way to the village. He was walking barefoot with his back straight and his head in the air. He had to walk carefully, because he was carrying a pile of clay pots on his head.

On one side of the road the sugar cane in the fields whispered softly as the wind blew through the leaves. On the other side of the road the banana plants nodded and waved. It seemed as though they were talking to Diego.

But Diego did not look toward the fields at all. He had helped with the planting of both the sugar cane and the banana plants, and he wanted nothing more to do with them. He hated the work in the fields.

Soon the time would come for harvesting the sugar cane. Cutting sugar cane from morning until night with a heavy knife, almost as long as himself, was no fun. He wished the harvest time would never come at all.

For a whole week now Diego had been working at the potter's wheel once used by his father. The pots he was carrying on his head today, he had made all by himself. Many Cubans made clay pots, but not pots like those Diego's father had made. Diego's father had been a famous potter. He had always painted his jars handsomely with clay of many colors.

Diego chuckled to himself. He had not told his mother that he had made these pots. Think how surprised she would be if he could sell them! Perhaps she would let him make pottery after that, instead of doing the hated work in the sugar fields.

"I hate bananas and sugar cane and pine-apples," Diego grumbled as he walked along. "I hate them. If only I could be a potter instead!"

Before Diego reached the village, many oxcarts rumbled past him. They were bringing in sugar cane, pineapples, and bunches of bananas from the plantations. Some loads were to be shipped to the mills, others to the packers.

The sugar cane was on the way to the mill. There the stalks would be squashed and rolled to press out the sweet juice, and the juice would later be boiled down into sugar.

Diego had once visited the sugar mill. He would never have believed, if he had not seen it himself, that fine white sugar could come out of the juice and the things that were mixed with it and boiled together.

Diego was thinking of that visit as he walked steadily along the road to market. He had been interested to see what happened to the cane before it went out into the world as sugar. But still he hated the work in the plantation fields. That part was hot and sticky and unpleasant.

When at last Diego arrived at the market, he found it a lively place. All about him were men and women displaying their goods in stalls or upon the ground. More were coming every minute, carrying upon their heads baskets of fruit, nuts, fish, or chickens, to be sold in the market.

Diego proudly spread his clay pots upon the paving stones of the street. He was certain some visitors from the north would be glad to buy them as presents to take home to the United States.

In a stall across the street was a man with tiny clay pots which he had made. Each pot held a small cactus plant. But the pots were all alike, and they were clumsy and very badly made.

"No one will want them," thought Diego.

As the day went on, the market place began to fill. Diego held out his pots with a bright smile, but the visitors from the United States passed them by. The small cactus plants in the ugly pots across the way interested them more.

"We're going to take them home to give to our friends," the strangers pointed out. "Then they can see the kind of plants that grow in Cuba."

One lady did stop before Diego's display, but looked at the pots a little sadly. "If they only had something growing in them," she said and walked on.

"They will surely not all like those ugly pots," Diego kept telling himself. "Someone will come to buy mine, and then others will follow."

But when evening came, not one of Diego's pots had been sold. He would have to walk all the way home again with them piled high on his head.

Double Doors

Diego gathered up his pots and started home. He was very much ashamed of himself. His father had been a fine pottery-maker. Yet his son was such a poor workman that he could not make a thing good enough to sell.

"Perhaps the pots are a bit crooked around the edges," a voice within him whispered.

Diego walked on a bit farther. Then he cried out, "No, my work is not poor and crooked!"

He had not walked much farther when he met old Franco. He was on his way to town, with a basket of fruit in either hand and a stack of hats balanced on his head.

"You're going the wrong way," Franco said. So Diego told him his troubles.

"Do not be so unhappy." Old Franco tried to comfort him. "Every difficulty has double doors. One door leads in, and so the other must lead out."

"It looks to me as though both doors lead in," Diego grumbled. But just the same, he began to feel a little less gloomy. He walked proudly again, the pots sitting easily on his head.

When he came to the pineapple plantation, he was so tired he sat down to rest. While he was sitting there, he looked down into a hollow beside the road. Some children had been playing there. Scattered boxes and empty cans showed that they had set up a store. In one tin can, half full of dirt, there was a pineapple plant growing.

Maybe the top of a pineapple had fallen into the can, or maybe the children had planted it. Anyway it had taken root and grown.

"It looks every bit as pretty as the cactus plants that man was selling in the market today," Diego thought with a chuckle.

Diego emptied the can into one of his clay pots. After he had filled the pot with dirt, he was surprised to see how nice it looked.

Then he had an idea. "I could plant bananas and sugar cane and pineapples in my pots. Then people could really see what grows in Cuba."

He gathered up his pots and hurried home.

It took a few days before Diego could get his potted garden to take root, but at last everything was ready. Diego set out for the village again. This time, however, he did not carry the pots on his head. He took his mother's ox and oxcart.

He had been in the market less than ten minutes when people from far and near gathered around his display.

"Won't you take one of these small pots of sugar cane with you?" they heard Diego call out in his high, clear voice. "Cuba is the most important sugar-cane country in the world." And he went on, "Here's a pineapple plant, and here's a small banana plant. Real Cuban plants in real Cuban pots!"

The visitors from the United States crowded closely around Diego.

304

"If we take these plants home with us, can we make them grow into full-grown banana plants?" they asked.

"No," said Diego, "not unless you keep them in a greenhouse. You see, they need lots of heat."

The strangers wanted to know about the sugar cane and the pineapple, too. In less than half an hour Diego had sold every pot he had. Many people were standing by, grumbling because there were no more of Diego's pots for them.

That day, as Diego rode home behind the old ox, he felt very happy and proud.

As he passed the plantations of sugar cane and bananas and pineapple, he bowed and said, "My friends, I think you will not see me so often after this, for I am going to be a pottery-maker like my father. But now I do not hate you any more. You helped me when I was in difficulty. Your little plants brought visitors to buy my pots. I will always think of you and thank you as I work at my wheel."

Diego smiled and bowed again. The sugar cane and the banana plants nodded gently back at him as though they had known all about it from the beginning.

Nora Burglon

Just Enough

Sarah's Idea

The harvest was almost over. It made Sarah feel somehow very lonesome, for the harvest had been fun. She and her younger sister, Linda, were walking through the lonely prune orchard.

Silently the two girls looked upon the cold campfire where the prune-pickers had cooked their food. A few early fall leaves were scattered about. Sarah kicked at them and saw three prunes roll ahead of her foot.

"Those prunes won't do anyone any good now." Linda sounded quite gloomy.

"I wonder if Father knows about it," Sarah said. "Maybe he hadn't noticed that they haven't all dropped off the trees yet. There goes one now."

As she spoke, a fat ripe prune fell at her feet.

Linda looked up excitedly. "Let's tell him," she said.

Glad of something interesting to do, the girls ran toward the drying field, where Father and Joe were piling trays of prunes.

"Father!" Linda began calling the moment he appeared from behind a pile of prune trays. "Father, there are still some prunes left in the orchard."

Father helped Joe to swing a tray of prunes into place before he turned to smile at Linda.

"I know," he said. "It does seem too bad. But you see, so few prunes are left that it wouldn't pay any men to pick them. They wouldn't make enough to pay for their time. There wouldn't be over ten boxes of fruit on the twenty acres."

"But isn't it good fruit?" Sarah asked.

"As good as any we have harvested," he answered.

Suddenly an idea blazed in Sarah's mind. Her heart began to thump loudly. It was such a splendid idea! If only Father would say yes to it! She tried to speak, but her mouth was all at once so dry that it couldn't make words. At last she swallowed hard and spoke in a strange voice, not at all like her own.

308

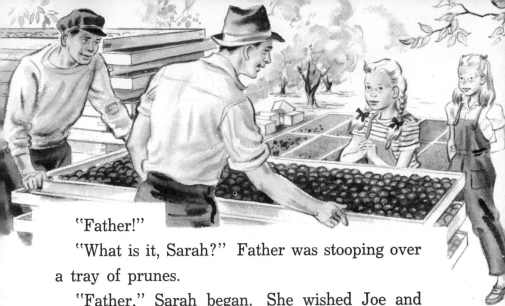

"Father!"

"What is it, Sarah?" Father was stooping over a tray of prunes.

"Father," Sarah began. She wished Joe and Linda weren't there. She was afraid they might laugh at her. The idea seemed silly now that she was about to put it into words.

"Well, Sarah?" Father was looking at her in a questioning way.

"Father, may I have the prunes that are left? I mean"—Sarah rushed on—"I mean, if I pick them up, may I have the money they will bring?"

Father laughed and turned back to his work.

"It's a good deal of a job, Sarah. You'd have to cover the whole orchard."

"I know," said Sarah. "But please let me."

She sounded as if she just had to do it, as if it were very important somehow.

309

Father straightened up to look at his daughter. He saw her dark eyes gazing hard at him, while she waited anxiously for his answer.

"All right," Father said slowly. "But unless you cover the whole orchard, I can't take the trouble to fire the lye pot and dip the prunes. All or nothing! Is it agreed?"

"Oh, yes," Sarah breathed happily. "And thank you, Father."

Sarah's Helper

Sarah was so excited she hardly knew what to do now that her wish seemed to be coming true. Instead of hurrying off to pick prunes as fast as possible, she just stood as if rooted to the ground.

Only one thought was perfectly clear to her. If she picked ten boxes of prunes, she could sell them, and with the money she could buy a burro. A gray burro with brown stripes over its shoulders! At last she could have the burro she had wanted for so long.

She felt as if she must shout her good luck to all the world. But she held her tongue. It was better to keep her secret until she had the money.

310

And then, right in the middle of her happy thoughts, she heard Linda saying, "I'll help you, Sarah. You'll get through much quicker if I help."

Sarah could hardly believe her ears. Think of Linda offering to pick prunes! Linda, who hated dirt, was saying that she wanted to crawl over twenty acres of it!

That was astonishing. But also it meant the end of Sarah's wish. For if Linda helped to pick the prunes, she would want half the money they brought. And Sarah was sure it would take every cent that ten boxes would bring to buy a burro.

"What's the matter, Sarah? Don't you want me to help you?" asked Linda.

Sarah glanced at her sister and was astonished to see that Linda's chin was quivering and her eyes were full of tears. Whatever was the matter?

"Don't you want me to help you?" she asked again in a queer, tight voice.

Sarah cleared her throat. "Yes, of course, Linda. Only I want the money for something very important. I—I need all the prunes myself."

She knew it sounded selfish and was glad Father and Joe had moved out of hearing.

311

Sarah really felt sorry for Linda, but Linda no longer seemed to feel sorry about anything. In the next glance Sarah saw that all her tears had gone. She was even smiling as happily as if something splendid had happened to her.

"Oh, I don't want a cent of the money, Sarah. I just want to help you. Truly!"

Sarah looked into Linda's clear eyes raised to hers, and suddenly she felt mean and small. In that second she knew that as long as she lived, she would never be as unselfish and fine as Linda, no matter how hard she tried.

But there was nothing to stop her trying. She would start right away, not by giving Linda half the money, but by making Linda a partner in the secret. They would buy a burro together. Why hadn't she thought of it before?

"I'll be very glad if you'll help, Linda," said Sarah.

"Shall we start right now?" Linda believed in never putting off anything.

"Let's," agreed Sarah, feeling as if a heavy lump of lonesomeness had melted away inside of her.

312

Partners at Work

Eager and excited, each girl took a row of trees. They started at the very back of the orchard, deciding that it would be more fun to work toward the house than away from it.

"We can play we're going to find the Promised Land," said Sarah. "The house and barn will be the Promised Land."

"And the prune picking will be the difficulties we go through," added Linda from the next row. Her face was quite red from stooping, but she was bravely keeping up with Sarah. Both girls were making the crisp leaves fly, shaking each tree for whatever fruit might still be hanging to its twigs and branches.

313

"Sarah, what are you going to do with the money when you get it?" asked Linda, pausing a moment to rest.

Sarah had been waiting for this question, and had kept the secret until the question should be asked. It made it easier.

"That's what I want to tell you," she said, crossing over from her row of trees to join Linda. "As long as you want to help, I've decided to let you be a partner with me. We're going to buy a burro."

Linda's blue eyes grew round. "Truly?" she gasped.

Sarah nodded.

"Did Father say yes?" questioned Linda.

"I haven't asked him," Sarah had to say.

"But maybe he won't let us have a burro." Linda put into words the very thing that Sarah just wouldn't believe. It was the thing her mind had kept turning away from.

"I'm sure he would if we had the money to buy one," Sarah said.

She was trying to believe so herself as much as to make Linda believe so.

314

"Well, anyway," said Linda, "let's ask him. Then if he won't let us, we can plan to do something else with the money. It's more fun working if you know what you are working for. I do hope he'll let us have the burro, though. You know, Sarah," she added after a short pause, "I think that's the best idea you've ever had."

Sarah thought so, too, but she kept from saying so. It was agreed that they would ask Father at noon when they went up to the house for lunch.

All morning Sarah felt a heavy lump in her stomach, and her throat tightened every time she thought of Father's saying no. The prunes meant nothing if they couldn't buy her a burro.

But that noon when they unfolded the plan to Father, he looked at them for a long minute. Then he said, in a pleased voice, that if two little girls wanted a burro badly enough to pick prunes for it, they ought to have one.

For the next week Sarah and Linda spent most of their time in the orchard picking their prunes. Linda was a splendid picker. One might almost have thought she enjoyed the work instead of disliking it.

315

But Linda believed in doing a hateful job as quickly as possible and being done with it. Because she was willing to pick prunes for Sarah didn't mean that she enjoyed it.

At last one day they came in sight of the Promised Land. Looking down the rows of trees, they could just about catch sight of the chicken yard, and back of it the red wall of the barn.

After that it seemed no time at all before the picking was finished, even to the last acre, and eleven boxes of prunes stood on the dipping platform. Sarah and Linda gazed proudly on their work.

Father was building a fire under the great tank full of lye and water into which the prunes would be dipped. Without this dipping, they would not keep.

"How long before the water will be hot?" questioned Linda.

"A few hours," Father answered. "Do you think you girls can feed the firebox while I go back to the drying field to help Joe?"

"Oh, yes," they both said at once.

Later, when the last prunes had been dipped into the lye pot and sorted, Father and Joe carried the trays of wet fruit off to the drying field and left the prunes there to dry in the hot sun.

"That's a fine lot of prunes," Father told the girls, "and I'm proud to think you harvested them all yourselves."

That made Sarah and Linda feel proud, too.

"Do you think they will bring enough money to buy a burro?" Linda asked.

Father paused and thought for a minute, while the sisters studied his face anxiously.

"You know, I believe they will," he said at last with a nod. "Yes, I'm almost certain that they'll bring just enough to buy a burro."

He sounded very sure, and even Joe, standing near, smiled at the good news.

317

That evening Sarah gave the empty stall in the red barn a specially good cleaning. She had been keeping it ready for this very day. She made the job last as long as she possibly could.

When she was done, she stood for a long while gazing into the stall. And clearer than ever before she could see a burro standing there, switching its tail.

A gray burro—a gray burro with brown markings over its shoulders!

Doris Gates

Pedro's House

A Visit to Uncle Manuel

Pedro lived in the Philippine Islands. He lived in a big white house in the city, where his grandmother worked for a rich family. Pedro worked sometimes, too. He kept the floors clean and shining, dusted the furniture, and ran here and there for everyone in the family.

Pedro was happy, but his grandmother sometimes said, "Rather would I have a little house of my own—just a wee house made of nipa palm."

"We'd build it high in the air on posts," Pedro would say, "with a ladder leading to the front door."

"And a banana tree growing ever so close to the window," said Grandmother.

"So close that I could eat bananas without going outdoors to pick them," Pedro added.

"Under the house," said Grandmother, "I'd have a bamboo pen, and there I'd keep my chickens. I've dreamed about the little house for so long, I can almost see it."

One day Uncle Manuel, who lived in the country, came to visit them.

"How are your rice fields?" Grandmother asked. "Have you planted yet?"

"Yes, we've planted," said Uncle Manuel. "My three girls and their mother are the best workers in the Philippines, but sometimes I'd like a boy —about as big as Pedro here."

"Pedro is a good boy, but he is very curious," said Grandmother. "And often his curiosity gets him into trouble."

Uncle Manuel laughed. "I'd like to take Pedro home with me," he said.

320

"Do you mean it, Uncle Manuel?" cried Pedro, for he had never been to the country and he was curious about it. "Do you want me to come?"

"Yes," said Uncle Manuel. "Our nipa house is small for the five of us, but a nipa house will stretch. There is always room for one more."

So Pedro went home with Uncle Manuel. When they reached his nipa house, it was dark. They stretched out on sleeping mats under mosquito nets.

Pedro woke early next morning, and at once he saw many things that made him curious. The house had very little furniture. And he could look right down through the cracks in the bamboo floor and see the back of the water buffalo that lived under the house. He could see some chickens in their bamboo pen and two black pigs.

Pedro could smell rice cooking. So he pulled aside his mosquito net and ran down the ladder at the door.

"Good morning," said Aunt Valentina. She was cooking breakfast on a stove out of doors.

Pedro's three girl cousins smiled at him and showed him where to wash his face.

They pulled down the end of a bamboo tube that hung from the roof, and caught the water in their hands.

After breakfast Pedro learned where to go to fill the bamboo tube with water at the well in the village. He learned how to pick the beans from which chocolate is made. He rode on the big water buffalo with his cousins.

On the far side of the rice fields near the river, they passed a grove of bamboo trees.

"We never stop here," said one of his cousins. "There's a haunted house in there."

"A real haunted house?" cried Pedro.

"That's what everyone says," she answered.

322

The Haunted House

In the weeks that followed, Pedro's curiosity got him into much trouble, just as it always had. But one day it brought him some luck.

It all happened because Pedro kept thinking about the haunted house among the bamboo trees by the river. No one would tell him about the house.

The more they said "You must never go near it," the more curious Pedro got. He wanted to see what a haunted house looked like—from a safe distance of course.

One sunny day Pedro walked bravely along the river road until he came to the grove of bamboo trees, waving their fine leaves and whispering to themselves. He waited awhile, half afraid to go on, and yet too curious to go away without even seeing the little house. From one bamboo tree to another he crept cautiously, until—he could just see the house.

Bamboo trees grew close around it, and a flowering tree threw its yellow blossoms like a scarf across the door.

Like sad, lonesome eyes, the windows stared out from under the worn old nipa roof. The little house sat in the tangled undergrowth as if it were half asleep and dreaming of the days when laughing children played about its door.

"It doesn't look haunted," thought Pedro. He moved a little nearer and hid behind the broad trunk of a palm tree. Nothing happened to him. He crept closer—almost to the door. Then he climbed up the shaky ladder and looked inside.

"It doesn't look haunted," Pedro said.

The sun, shining through the leaves of a banana tree at the window, sent long shadows across the bamboo floor.

"It's just the kind of house Grandmother has always wanted," said Pedro.

His voice sounded so loud in the quiet of the wood that he jumped to the ground. The sharp sound of the crisp dried palm leaves underfoot frightened him. Then he heard a noise in the palm tree above him. Without looking up to see what it was, Pedro turned and ran.

He scampered through the bamboo grove and down to the riverbank. Even out on the road he could hear something swishing through the trees as if it were following him. As he raced past the field of sugar cane, he heard the thing jump to the road. His curiosity overcame his fear, and he threw a quick glance over his shoulder.

Behind him was a monkey in a jacket, who came up to him and put his head on one side as if to say, "What is the matter, Pedro?"

Pedro sat down in the middle of the road, for his knees shook so that he couldn't stand up. The monkey climbed on his knee and took his finger. "I was only playing," he seemed to say to Pedro.

Then Pedro started to laugh. With the monkey in his arms, he laughed so loudly all the way home that his three cousins heard him coming and ran to meet him.

"Look what I have," cried Pedro.

"It's Magellan," cried one of the girls. "I know him by his jacket. He belongs to the *Señor* who lives in the big house near the church."

"I found him near the little old nipa house in the bamboo grove by the river," Pedro said.

"The haunted house!" cried the girls all together. "You didn't go there?"

"Yes, and it's nothing," said Pedro, feeling very brave.

"Weren't you scared?" asked one of the girls in a whisper.

"No," said Pedro. "It's just like any other old empty house. I wonder who owns it."

"I think it belongs to Magellan's *Señor* in the big house," said Aunt Valentina.

Suddenly Pedro had an idea. Magellan might help him. He decided to say nothing about it to the grownups, but after supper he told the three girls about it. When they had whispered awhile, Pedro took the monkey in his arms, and the girls led the way to the big house near the church.

It looked quite dark, but when Pedro knocked, the door was opened, and a servant in a white apron looked out at them. Before Pedro could say a word, Magellan jumped to the ground, bounded through the man's outstretched arms, and ran into the hall.

"Oh, Magellan!" cried a woman's voice from inside. "Where have you been?" She came to the door with the monkey in her arms and smiled at the four children. "Come in," she said.

They followed the *Señora* through a hall, then up some broad stairs to a balcony, and into a room where the *Señor* sat reading.

"Look! These children have brought Magellan home," cried the woman.

The little monkey bounded to the man's shoulder and put his head close to his ear.

"Where did you find him?" the *Señor* asked, as he patted the monkey's back.

"In the haunted house," answered Pedro.

"What were you doing there?" asked the *Señor*.

"I—I just wanted to see what it was like," explained Pedro.

"Weren't you afraid to go there?"

"No, it's just like any other house, only old."

"What's your name, boy?"

"Pedro."

"Well, Pedro, I like you. You're one boy who doesn't believe foolish stories. Thank you for finding Magellan and bringing him home."

The *Señor* held out a silver piece for Pedro.

"Thank you," said Pedro, "I don't want any money, but that little house is just the kind of house my grandmother has always wanted."

"Yes?" said the *Señor*.

"And we could mend it," Pedro hurried on. "I haven't any money to pay for it, but I could work for you. I could clean your floors every day before I go to school."

The man glanced at the *Señora* and smiled. "It seems to me that would be plenty to pay for the old house," he said.

"Do you mean it?" cried Pedro.

"Yes, of course, but don't let the house fall down on you." The man laughed and patted Pedro's head. "I like you, Pedro. Do whatever you want with the little old house."

"Oh, thank you," cried Pedro. He and the three girls went down the stairs and out into the moonlight. Pedro was too excited to talk. A house for Grandmother!

A House for Grandmother

Early the next morning the whole family went down to the bamboo grove to see Pedro's house.

Pedro was proud to show it to them, old and worn-out though it was. To be sure, it was very small, but Grandmother had always wanted a wee nipa house. There were four windows, one on each side, and a door. In the open place beneath the house, Grandmother could keep her chickens.

"It's a bit broken down," said Uncle Manuel, shaking the old ladder by the front door.

"And there are holes in the roof, and the floor sags in the middle," said one of the girls.

"Oh, but we can fix it!" cried Pedro. "We can mend the holes and make a new ladder."

"Well, you children go to work," said his uncle. "There's plenty of bamboo and nipa palm around."

"There's a coconut and a banana tree too," said Aunt Valentina. "So Pedro can have bananas."

With great joy Pedro and the three girls started mending the house for their grandmother. Before they knew it, the bamboo grove had become the most exciting place in the village.

330

It was like a new game. After school all the boys and girls raced down to the river to see who could help. Building a house by themselves was fun.

The boys borrowed their fathers' knives and cut down the bamboo shoots and tangled undergrowth in the yard. The girls brought nipa-palm leaves and helped Pedro mend the holes in the walls.

With the help of Uncle Manuel, they made four new shutters, weaving long pieces of bamboo into mats and tying them tightly with palm. Each shutter they hung by rings on a bamboo pole, so that it could be slipped back along the wall of the house or propped out to make a window shade.

Finally the parents heard so much about Pedro's house that they too came to the bamboo grove by the river. They came to watch, but they stayed to help.

331

Some said the work should be done this way, and others that way. Very soon they were putting up new poles to make the house steadier and weaving new pieces of bamboo into the sagging floor to make it firmer.

There was little need for furniture inside the house. Few country people in the Philippines have tables and chairs. Grandmother would have her own mats and mosquito nets and a basket for her clothes. Everything seemed to be ready.

But one day the ropemaker and his wife came to see what was happening in the bamboo grove.

"Oh," said the ropemaker, "I see you have a fine house there."

"But what about a kitchen?" said his wife. "Now to my mind, every house needs a kitchen. You can't live on bananas day in and day out."

"I forgot about a kitchen," said Pedro. "Maybe we could build an open fire when we want to cook."

"No, you must have a stove," said the ropemaker. Then the two of them trudged home and brought back their present for Grandmother's nipa house.

332

The ropemaker put an earthen pot down on the ground by the door. "That's for the fire," he said.

His wife put another earthen pot on top and said, "That's for the rice and the fish and the stew. Now you have a kitchen."

For plates Pedro knew that Grandmother could use banana leaves, and for cups and bowls she could use coconut shells. It was very easy, for they grew right in the yard.

Then Aunt Valentina came with a feast for all the children. She had a basketful of coconut cakes and sweetened rice sticks. She made a fire in the lower part of Pedro's new stove, and in the pot on top she put ground-up chocolate beans mixed with sugar and water. In no time at all there was a pot full of hot chocolate, and each child found a coconut shell for a cup.

Finally the house was ready and waiting to surprise Grandmother. They wrote a letter inviting her to come for a visit, but of course they said not a word about the little nipa house. They only asked her to bring her sleeping mat and her mosquito net.

As soon as Grandmother arrived, Pedro and the whole family took her to see the little nipa house. Sitting in the middle of a clean yard, it looked as if it had just been waiting for her.

"It's for you," said Pedro.

"Oh-h-h," breathed Grandmother. "What a dear little house!" Then she turned to her grandson. "What did you say, Pedro?"

"It's for you, Grandmother."

Suddenly everyone was explaining at once how Pedro had found the little house and how the whole village had helped mend it for her.

Grandmother was so astonished she couldn't say a word. But her shining eyes told everyone she was too happy to speak. And as for Pedro— he was the happiest boy in the Philippines.

Esther Wood

334

Lincoln

There was a boy of other days,
A quiet, awkward, earnest lad,
Who trudged long weary miles to get
A book on which his heart was set—
And then no candle had!

He was too poor to buy a lamp,
But very wise in woodmen's ways.
He gathered seasoned bough and stem,
And crisping leaf, and kindled them
Into a ruddy blaze.

335

Then as he lay full length and read,
The firelight flickered on his face,
And etched his shadow on the gloom,
And made a picture in the room,
In that most humble place.

The hard years came, the hard years went,
But gentle, brave, and strong of will,
He met them all. And when today
We see his pictured face, we say,
"There's light upon it still."

Nancy Byrd Turner

Kate of Hungary

Exciting News

Kate had come to live with her cousin Jancsi and her aunt and uncle on a ranch in Hungary.

The apple trees were in full blossom. White strawberry flowers covered the edge of the pastures. The farmyard was busy with new life. Baby chicks ran about in the grass. Pink little pigs squealed in their pen. The cow had a brown-and-white calf, marked like a chestnut. It kept tumbling after its mother and getting in everybody's way.

The vegetable garden was coming along well. The fresh green plants were standing in even rows, like so many little green soldiers. Swallows darted under the porch, repairing their nests.

Kate was having a wonderful time, planting a flower garden all her own. She could hardly wait for the baby plants to grow.

One day when Kate's uncle came home from the village, he said, "I have a surprise for all of you. I heard that the big fair will be held near our village this year, one week from today."

"Oh! And may we all go?" asked Jancsi, the boy cousin who had taught Kate to ride.

"Of course we shall go, but first I have to get some horses for the animal show. I'm riding out to the herds across the river to round up about twenty. I want to sell some at the fair. Jancsi, you're coming with me. And if Kate wants to leave her garden for a day, she may come along."

Kate looked at her aunt. "Will the baby flowers be safe if I leave them?" she asked.

"Don't you worry, child. I'll take good care of them," said her aunt, smiling.

Early the next morning they rode out of the yard while the dew was still sparkling on the grass.

There were large grainfields on both sides of the road they took. Narrow paths forked off from the road, leading to white cottages resting under big shade trees. From a distance the cottages with their heavy straw roofs looked like small white toadstools.

The landscape slowly changed as they rode along. There were more and more trees. They crossed many small wooden bridges over sparkling brooks. Soon they could see the river, like a wide blue ribbon on the soft green of the fields.

Jancsi rode ahead. Then he waved and cried, "The ferry is in. Hurry! They're waiting for us."

They drove their horses faster and trotted noisily on to the floating ferry. It was fastened to stout ropes on both sides. The ropes stretched across the river and were wound on large wooden wheels. There were several wagons and riders on the wide platform of the ferry.

Kate, following her uncle and Jancsi, got off her horse and tied him to a post.

"How shall we get across? Row?" she asked.

"Watch these men, Kate. They'll pull the ferry across by the ropes. We can help," said Jancsi.

A bell sounded. Another answered from across the river. Everybody walked to the ropes.

"Here, Kate. Take this rope!" said Jancsi. "Pull when they say 'Hooo-ruck!'"

"Hooo-ruck! Hooo-ruck!" sang out everybody as they pulled on the ropes. The far bank seemed to come nearer and nearer. They could see other wagons and riders waiting. There was a dragging sound when the ferry touched bottom and came to a stop. A man on the bank fastened it to a post.

"Coming back tonight, Mister Nagy?" the ferryman asked Kate's uncle when they rode past him.

"Yes," her uncle told the ferryman. "We'll bring about twenty horses. Please wait for us."

The Roundup

The road wound through a small forest. The branches of the trees were heavy with bunches of white flowers. The air was filled with their sweet, heavy smell. White blossoms drifted in the breeze, covering the ground like snowflakes.

As soon as the riders left the forest, they saw the first corrals. These were huge grassy squares, with tall fences around them. Long, low stables and a few white cottages were scattered among the corrals. In the distance hundreds of horses were grazing quietly. Here and there a horse-herder sat his horse, still as a statue against the blue sky.

Suddenly one of the statues rode over to where Kate and her uncle and Jancsi were waiting. He was an old man, but he was straight and strong, with snow-white hair and a sunburned face. His black eyes were sharp as an eagle's.

"Welcome, Mister Nagy. We got your message. The boys are ready for the roundup." He looked at Kate and Jancsi. "The young ones could stay with my wife, out of danger."

Kate's uncle shook his head. "Jancsi is working with us this year. He is old enough to know what it's all about. But—Kate, I think you'd better stay with Arpad's wife."

"Oh, Uncle, please let me go, too. Please!" cried Kate.

Her uncle looked at the old herder. Arpad shook his head.

"It's too dangerous. If those horses stampede, Mister Nagy, you know what it means! A roundup is no place for a girl child."

"She isn't a girl child. She's almost as good as a boy," said her cousin Jancsi stoutly. "Father, let Kate ride with me. I can take care of her."

His father paused for a second. Then he said, "Kate, will you promise to keep close to Jancsi and not to scream or yell no matter what happens?" He spoke quite anxiously. "If these wild horses hear one of your special brand of screams, they'll run right off the face of the earth."

342

"I promise!" said Kate, looking straight into his eyes.

"Very well, you may go with Jancsi. Arpad, you take two men and start the drive from the north. Send four men to me. Two will go with Jancsi and Kate and drive from the east. I'll take two men to the west."

Arpad's straight back looked as if he were very unhappy about the whole thing, when he rode away. They saw him stop and speak to the men.

"Jancsi!" His father's voice rang sharp. "You are one of the men today. Do you know what to do?"

"Yes, Father. I ride slowly to the east fields about two miles from here. When I pass the last herds, I turn and start the drive back to the corrals. If they stampede, I ride with them and try to take the lead to turn the herd."

"If they stampede, you take Kate out of the way and let the herders turn them. Understand?"

343

Then he gave orders to the waiting herders, and they rode off.

Kate and Jancsi silently followed the two young herders. They rode slowly, keeping well away from the grazing horses. Kate watched the men. She wondered if they ever got off their horses or were grown to them. They sat straight in their saddles, and their bodies followed the swinging movement of the horses in smooth, perfect timing.

Jancsi touched her arm and whispered, "You won't scream, Kate?" He looked worried.

"I won't make a sound, no matter what happens. Thank you for sticking up for me."

A tall fence showed in the distance. "Here's where we spread out," said one of the herders.

Kate was much excited. "Stampede, stampede," kept ringing in her ears. "If they stampede—"

But everything went well. They turned back toward the corrals. There was a little stir and movement in the herd as they came nearer. The horses stopped grazing and neighed uneasily, but they weren't frightened. Slowly they began to move toward the corrals.

344

A Stampede

Jancsi and Kate were right behind the horses, the herders a little to the sides. Jancsi took off his hat and dried his forehead. His first roundup was going off well, and he felt very proud. Surely there wouldn't be any trouble.

But—what was the sudden stir in front there? Jancsi saw a flock of birds fly up, heard the sharp, frightened neighing of the lead horses, and saw the whole herd sway and turn.

"They're turning! Get out of the way, Kate! Follow me!" he ordered.

It was too late. The herd was thundering down on them. He couldn't stop to help Kate. His own horse had caught the herd's fright and was running at top speed. Looking around, he saw Kate's horse flash by and turn to the right with Kate bent close to his neck.

345

Jancsi shouted, "To the left, Kate!"

It was no use. He could hardly hear his own voice over the thunder of the horses' hoofs. His own words flashed in his mind, "If they stampede, I take the lead to turn the herd!"

Using all his might, he got his horse to turn to the right. The herd followed! "Now back to the corrals, if I can only keep ahead of them!"

Jancsi dug his heels into the horse's sides. Almost flying over the pasture, he turned his head to look for Kate. Why, the herd must have broken in half! There was Kate to his far right, racing ahead of more horses than he had behind him! She was leading them to the corrals!

"What a girl!" shouted Jancsi. "Hooray!"

Jancsi was almost at the first corral gate. He pulled his horse sharply to one side. The wild horses thundered past him and raced around into the corral. He closed the gate quickly, just as the rest of the herd rushed into the next corral. Kate's horse, shivering and snorting, pressed close to Jancsi's horse.

Kate grinned at Jancsi as she closed the gates. "Look at the herders," she said with a laugh. "We beat them to it."

The two men looked a little silly and a bit upset. There was no time for talk, though. Father's herd came in, closely followed by old Arpad's from the north.

When all the horses were safely closed behind the gates, a cottage door opened, and Arpad's wife came out ringing a bell.

"Dinner's ready," she cried.

Father turned to the silent herders. "How did my young ones behave?"

The herders grinned. "Behave, Mister Nagy? Behave? Why, the two of them turned the worst stampede we ever saw and brought the herd in before we knew what had happened."

"What?" cried Arpad and Father together.

"I didn't scream, did I, Jancsi?" cried Kate.

"She didn't, Father. A flock of birds started them off. But can she ride! She rides almost as well as you!"

"That's saying a lot, sonny." Old Arpad smiled. "Your father is the best horseman in this part of Hungary. But tell us all about it while we eat."

They got off their horses and walked to the cottage. In the doorway Arpad took off his hat. "Welcome to my house and table," he said.

"Welcome, and thank God you are all here," cried his wife. "When I saw this girl child ahead of the horses, I feared the worst. I thought we'd be picking her up in little pieces instead of sitting down to dinner! My, my, what is this world coming to! When I was her age, I had to sit by the window and sew all day, and here she is, no bigger than a bee, racing with the best of you. Oh, oh, I shouldn't chatter. You must be very hungry!"

"Sit down and welcome," said Arpad.

He said a prayer, and then a huge bowl of steaming stew was set on the table.

"Now, let's hear the story," said Father, when everyone's plate was filled.

Jancsi laughed. "The story of a bee on horseback!"

Little by little the story was pieced together. "But how did you know what to do, Kate?" asked Father.

"There was nothing else to do," she said quietly. "I remembered what Jancsi said about taking the lead if they stampeded. I didn't have to take it —they chased me!" She grinned. "Then we came to the horse yards—"

"Corrals, Kate," broke in Jancsi.

"Corrals, then. Anyway, I saw you pull your horse to one side. So I did the same thing. It was easy!"

Old Arpad shook his head. "The good God watched over you, child. You were in great danger."

They were all silent a long time. Then Father spoke. "I shouldn't have let you go, Kate, but now that everything is over, I am very proud of both of you."

Kate Seredy

350

Exploring Nature's Secrets

The Birds That Earned a Home

Gulls to the Rescue

It was about a hundred years ago that the first settlers came to the Great Salt Lake valley. Because they had left cities and stores far behind, they had brought seeds with them from the East to grow their own grain for food.

The second year, when their grain was almost ready to gather, a frightening thing happened. Thousands upon thousands of crickets appeared. They were not the kind of cricket that hops about in our gardens. They were a kind of big black cricket that eats wheat, corn, and other grain.

They came hopping across the fields in moving black lines, eating everything before them. What could the farmers do? They saw their winter store of food vanishing. Unless it was saved, the people would go hungry and die.

Madly the settlers fought the crickets, killing thousands of them, but thousands more of the hungry creatures remained.

Suddenly, as if by magic, a cloud appeared— a cloud of white wings.

352

Thousands of hungry gulls, that nested on islands in the Great Salt Lake, flew down upon the fields and began to gobble the crickets. In a little while every cricket had vanished. The grain had been saved.

The people gave thanks to God. And years later their grandsons built a monument to help everyone remember how the gulls saved the grain.

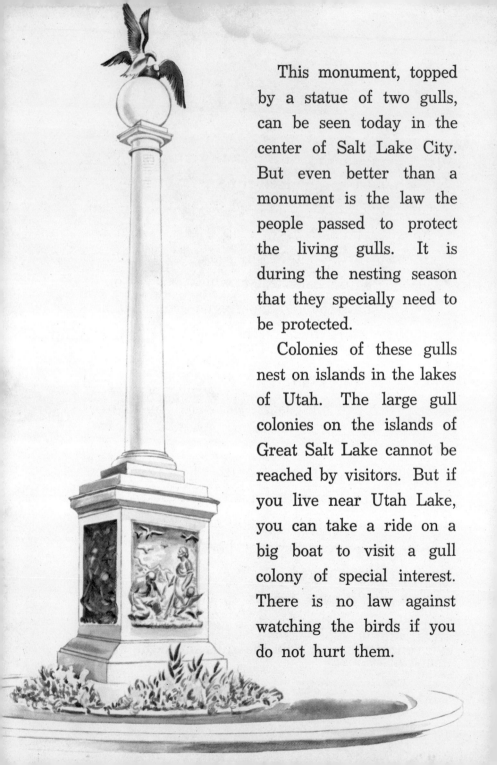

This monument, topped by a statue of two gulls, can be seen today in the center of Salt Lake City. But even better than a monument is the law the people passed to protect the living gulls. It is during the nesting season that they specially need to be protected.

Colonies of these gulls nest on islands in the lakes of Utah. The large gull colonies on the islands of Great Salt Lake cannot be reached by visitors. But if you live near Utah Lake, you can take a ride on a big boat to visit a gull colony of special interest. There is no law against watching the birds if you do not hurt them.

An Island Home

The boat ride to Rock Island in Utah Lake, where the gulls live, lasts about two hours. Along with a hundred or more other people, you may take a picnic lunch and spend a whole day on the trip.

Rock Island is a very small island, which has been made in an interesting way. Utah Lake is filled mostly by cold water which rushes down from the snow-covered mountains around it and partly by water which rushes up through the lake bed from springs deep within the earth. The water from these springs is full of a certain mineral which, through the years, has piled up until it has made an island.

It is on the light-gray rock of this mineral island that the gulls have their nests.

If someone drew a map of this island for gulls, you would see that it is shaped very much like a gull. To the southwest its wings are about three city blocks long from tip to tip. To the southeast it has a tail two blocks long. However, when the water of the lake is high, as it often is, this gull shape disappears.

355

There is a line of trees along the part of the island that is shaped like the body of a gull. Little plants two feet high cover some of the rocks. The seeds for these plants have been blown here from shore, and sand and earth washed up from the lake have helped them to take root.

While you are still several miles away from Rock Island, you will see a few gulls, for they fly out to meet the boat. If food is to be had, a trip of many miles means nothing to them. And they are always looking for food.

They fly over the boat, sometimes working their wings hard, sometimes coasting on the wind. The gulls seem to float on the air as easily as the boat floats on the waters of Utah Lake.

They keep their heads turned toward the boat, their sharp eyes watching for something to eat. As soon as any food is thrown into the air and out over the water, there is a wild rush of wings. Since the gulls cannot dive like ducks, they must catch the food in the air or on the surface of the water.

If the piece of food is very large, the gull cannot eat it all in one bite. So his fellows chase him, hoping he will drop it. Everyone enjoys seeing the gulls at this game.

Since gulls do not like oranges, people often play tricks on them by throwing pieces of orange.

First one gull catches the piece of orange in his yellow bill, while his fellows rush after him. When he finds out what it is, he drops his prize and flies up over the boat again. But right away another gull speeds down to the piece of orange and takes it away in his bill. Close after him rush more hungry gulls. This happens over and over again before the gulls seem to learn that it is a trick.

These gulls, like all lake and sea gulls, with their long, narrow wings and their streamline bodies, are Nature's airplanes. Their wings stretch about three feet from tip to tip, and their bodies are just a little more than a third as long. Their tails are short and square at the end.

Their webbed feet make them good swimmers, and their feathers keep their bodies dry. While they are flying high over the boat, their bodies seem all white, but when they come down closer, you can see that their backs are a soft gray. There are black markings near the tip of each wing. Their legs and webbed feet are a light yellow.

At last the boat reaches the mineral island, and everybody starts to get off. The gulls do not welcome you. They fly about excitedly and cry out angrily and loudly. They do not seem to like it that you have come. They stay high up above their nests, peering down at you with hard, glassy eyes.

There are thousands of them. They fly wing to wing without touching each other. They dive, they circle, they glide, but still they keep out of each other's way. They also keep out of your way.

Nests and Baby Gulls

With everybody else, you start toward the southwest end of the gull-shaped island. There most of the nests have been made, because that is the warmer, less windy side. Everyone is seeking for eggs. But if your trip is late in June, most of the baby gulls will have hatched.

Even though they cannot fly at all or even walk very well, still they can make their way over the rocks with their little black webbed feet. You may even see some of them paddling near the shore.

Later they lose their first black-spotted baby feathers. The new fluffy feathers that stand out all over them make the baby gulls look even bigger than their parents.

You find the nests on the rocks very close together, but they do not look much like nests. Any little low place in the rocks that can keep an egg from rolling seems to have been used for a nest and lined with grass, sticks, fluff, or feathers—whatever was at hand.

In and around some nests there are feathers and small shells and cherry stones. The parent gulls eat fish, insects, worms, and nearly anything they can find. They must bring food to the island for their young. The cherry stones are from cherries they have got in orchards miles away, where they flew looking for food.

Perhaps at first you do not see any eggs among the rocks, but at last you find what you are seeking. In a nest are two gray-brown eggs a little larger than a hen's egg. They are spotted a dark brown that is almost a purple.

Most gulls lay three eggs, and it may be that there were three in this nest and that one of them has hatched. A baby gull that you have seen may have come from this nest.

All too soon a loud whistle sounds. Everyone hurries toward the boat. As it leaves, some of the parent gulls fly down to sit once more on their eggs. Many of them follow the boat on the two-hour trip back to shore, and you throw them pieces of food left over from your lunch.

During the trip back, you all sing songs, and you watch the lake and the mountains and the sky as the sun goes down. The nearer mountains turn a deep purple, while those far away look light blue. Turquoise blue and deep blue fill the sky. The clouds turn yellow and orange and purple under the magic of coming night. A new moon high in the sky looks like a little orange cloud itself.

And still the gulls are with you. Their strong white wings, lined with silver in the moonlight, make a rushing sound in the wind. For with night the wind has come, and the gray-green water is no longer quiet.

362

As the boat nears the shore, the gulls turn, one by one, like airplanes, and head back toward their island home.

Did you see that there are metal bands on the legs of some of these gulls? These metal bands are put on by men who study birds. These men learn by banding some of the gulls just where they go for the winter and whether the same gulls come back the next summer. The gulls that nest on Rock Island fly to California and other shores along the Pacific Ocean to spend the winter.

When you get off the boat this June evening, you are feeling happy because of all the interesting and exciting things you have seen. And you feel good to remember the nesting place of these gulls that helped our early farmers save their grain and so earned their right to a safe home.

Constance M. McCullough

Workers Underground

No boy or girl who has ever gone fishing needs to be told that earthworms are good for something. Everyone knows that fish like worms better than almost anything else. But it is so easy to catch a fish with an earthworm that the best fishermen will not use worms at all. They say that anyone can catch a fish with a worm. So they use something else, and that makes fishing more exciting.

But the first fish you ever caught was very likely caught with an earthworm. And today, if you were to think about going fishing, the chances are that you would start at once to find a can and fill it with soil and earthworms.

But earthworms are good for something besides fish bait. They help to make the soil better for growing things.

Did you ever look carefully at the places where you were digging for worms? You may have been too busy looking for the worms to look at the ground they lived in. But if you were wise, you started digging first in a damp place. Earthworms like moist soil. And when it dries out on top, they just dig deeper into the ground to where the soil is moist.

As earthworms crawl through the damp earth, they take little pieces of it into their bodies. These little pieces of soil pass through their food organs and are then thrown out again. Sometimes the soil is thrown up to the top of the ground and looks like moist balls of earth, almost too small to see. You may have noticed some of these tiny balls, left in a bunch on the ground.

With thousands of earthworms sending out these millions of balls of earth, the soil is broken. It is then easy for plants to send their roots down into the soil, just as it is easier for you to dig in it.

365

Some people grow earthworms for a living, just as other people grow chickens or turkeys or rabbits.

"But why?" you ask. "Earthworms are everywhere. Why should anyone grow them?"

But earthworms do not live everywhere. In some places the soil has become so hard and dry that worms cannot live in it.

Farmers know that a soil without earthworms may become a soil without plants. So they go to work on that soil. They break its hard surface. They work plant food into it. And many of them send away for the eggs of earthworms to put into the soil to make it better for planting.

Earthworms must be grown as carefully as any plant. This is how it is done.

First a bed of rich soil and plant food is made. It looks very much like a flower bed. Then layers of rough cloth, such as potato sacks are made of, are put into the bed of soil. Of course the cloth is sprinkled to make it damp, because earthworms like it that way. Then the earthworms are placed on the damp cloth, and that is where they lay their eggs.

366

The eggs are laid in tiny bunches. Millions of them can be mailed in a small box. These boxes are sent to any part of the world—Arizona, Maryland, Florida, Australia—wherever the soil is in need of earthworms.

The farmer who gets the eggs puts them into the ground, and in one month millions of earthworms begin to crawl through the soil, breaking it up and giving it food for plants. Good plants begin to grow where poor plants grew before.

Since earthworms are so hard to find in some places and easy to find in others, it looks as if growing earthworms might be a good thing for boys and girls to do.

And think how fine it would be next time you went fishing, just to go out in your own back yard to your very own bed of earthworms, roll back the cloth, and pick up a handful of worms!

Doris Gates

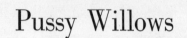

Pussy Willows

I came on them yesterday (merely by chance),
Those newly born pussies, asleep on a branch;
Each curled up so tight in a fluff of a ball
That I could not see ear-points or tail-tips at
   all;
But I thought that I heard, when the March wind
   was stirring,
A soft little sound like the low note of purring.
I wonder if they would have leaped from their
   bough
And arched their wee backs with a frightened
   "Meow!"
If I had dared tell them in one warning cry
That a fierce patch of dogwood was growing
   close by.

Rowena Bastin Bennett

Digger, Prairie Mole

The winter weather did not trouble Digger, the prairie mole. All the field was covered with snow, but Digger did not shovel any of it when he hurried along his path one morning. He didn't need to dig the snow, for his path was a tunnel under the ground.

Digger was hungry, and he ran until he found some eggs for his breakfast. The first egg case he came to had two dozen eggs in it, and Digger ate them all. Two dozen eggs may seem like a very big breakfast, but really they were not large eggs. A grasshopper had laid them.

The mother grasshopper that laid those eggs lived in grassy places while the weather was warmer, before the snow came. It was summer when she pushed the end of her body into the ground and laid the twenty-four eggs that Digger ate for his breakfast. The grasshopper did not put all her eggs into one case. She made several holes in the ground, and she left a case full of eggs in each hole.

There were thousands and thousands of grass-hoppers in Digger's part of the country that summer. So there were a great many egg cases in the ground. Digger and other prairie moles ate more eggs than usual that year.

Some years there were not so many grasshopper eggs. And what did Digger do then?

Usually there was plenty of other food for him in the ground. He liked the white grubs that change into shiny brown May beetles when they grow up. Really he liked insects of almost any kind, and earthworms too.

Digger had a strange way of hunting in his tunnel. He could smell the earthworms and grubs, but he could not see them.

Digger's eyes were so small that they were almost no eyes at all, and they were hidden in the thick fur that covered most of his face. Since he could hunt without seeing, it didn't matter to him that his tunnel was dark. He needed no light at all.

His brown fur made a soft coat for Digger. This fur could be pushed toward his head as easily as toward his tail. There was no danger of rubbing Digger's fur the "wrong way."

His tail was not furry. There were so few short hairs on it that it looked almost naked. His feet had a little hair on top, but they were bare beneath. The end of his long snout was naked, too. He measured eight inches from the tip of his snout to the tip of his tail.

No one could tell where Digger's tunnel was while the ground was covered with snow. But when the snow melted in the spring, it was easy enough to find most of his runway. The top of it showed like a little curved ridge along the field.

If you had stood near by then, you could have seen the ground move up as Digger shoved ahead at the end of his new tunnel.

371

Digger pushed his strong snout into the soil at the end of his runway. Next he reached ahead with one broad front foot and shoved the dirt aside with it. Then he pushed in the same way with his other front foot. He moved almost as if he were swimming in the moist soil. He made his tunnel longer and longer.

That was the way Digger went hunting in the springtime. Perhaps first he would find a fat white grub lying on its curved back and reaching up as it chewed the roots of grasses and other plants. Next there might be a delicious cutworm or a narrow wireworm.

He did a good day's work for the farmers as he hunted for grubs and caterpillars that kill plants by eating their roots. Because of Digger and other moles, there were not so many white grubs left to grow into May beetles. There were not so many wireworms to become click beetles.

372

But Digger knew nothing whatever about the farmers' war against grubs or about the way he was helping the plants to grow. He just hunted because he was hungry and liked the taste of these little underground creatures.

Often, too, he found earthworms, which he also enjoyed. The earthworms spent the winter deep in the ground below the frost, but they came near the surface when the frost in the ground melted in the spring.

Although Digger was so hungry that he hunted most of the time, day and night, he did rest now and then. He had a nest about two feet down in the ground, under an old tree. He could run into his nest from his tunnels.

Digger hunted alone and rested alone. That is, he was alone most of the year.

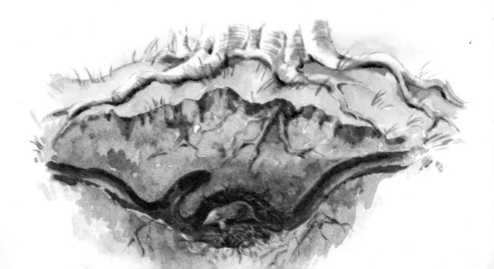

One spring night Digger did something different. He did not shove his snout into the soft soil at the end of his tunnel and "swim" ahead with his strong front feet. Instead, he pushed his snout through the roof of his tunnel and came up to the surface of the ground.

That night Digger went hunting in the open field, where he could go in any direction without making a tunnel to run in. For supper he found some spiders and insects that were creeping about.

Other prairie moles were hunting in that same field that same night in early spring.

Digger and another prairie mole became mates. And after a while the Digger family numbered six instead of two. Besides Digger and his mate, there were four baby Diggers that were born some time in May.

The baby Diggers had a cozy, lazy life in their hidden nest home while they were small. These fat, wrinkled, naked little moles were not able to hunt for their food. But of course their mother did not let them go hungry. She gave them all the milk they wanted to drink.

By the time they were a few weeks old they were no longer wrinkled and naked. They were then fully grown and clothed in fur and were able to go hunting for insects and earthworms.

They did not share the food they found. Each young Digger ran alone while he hunted in his tunnel. So when one of them found a case of new-laid grasshopper eggs, he did not call his brother and sisters to share the feast with him. He ate the whole two dozen eggs himself.

Edith M. Patch
Carroll Lane Fenton

The Eagle

He clasps the crag with crooked hands;
Close to the sun in lonely lands,
Ringed with the azure world, he stands.

The wrinkled sea beneath him crawls;
He watches from his mountain walls,
And like a thunderbolt he falls.

Alfred Tennyson

Animals' Eyes

The Hunters and the Hunted

Many questions about animals can be explained
if we remember that their way of life is very
different from ours. The most important things
they have to do are to find and capture their
food. The weaker are always trying to escape
from being food for the larger and stronger.

Animals have no policemen to protect them,
and there are no shops where they can buy food.
Each animal has to protect himself and to keep
his own shop. But Nature has given to each a
way of getting food and a way of protecting
himself which is exactly suited to his way of
living.

Some animals are furnished with better means
for capturing their food, while other animals have
better means for protecting themselves.

To the first group belong all the hunters.
Among them are the dog family, such as the fox
and the wolf, and the cat family, such as the lion,
the tiger, and the leopard. Many others, among
them the bear, belong in this group of hunters.

To the second group belong the hunted animals, from the tall giraffe to the tiny mouse. Deer, woodchucks, possums, muskrats, toads, and many other animals are in this group.

Front Eyes and Side Eyes

When we put animals into these two groups, the hunters and the hunted, it is easy to see the reason for some of the differences among them.

The eyes show some of the most interesting differences. If an animal hunts for its food, it must have eyes that look straight ahead. If you have ever seen a cat watching a mouse hole, or a dog chasing a rabbit, you can understand why their eyes are placed squarely in front.

At the same time you have the answer to another question. Side eyes are for the hunted creatures, who must protect themselves from danger that may come from each side as well as from the front.

Eyes for the Dark

You can find other interesting differences in animals' eyes if you study them. Look at the dark spot, called the pupil, in the very center of the eye. The pupil is really an opening that lets in the light to the back part of the eye.

The cat likes best to seek his food at night. So the pupil of his eye must open as widely as possible to let in what little night light there is. The pupil of the cat's eye is shaped somewhat like a round window with a looped curtain. When it is wide open, much light enters the eye.

But if Nature had not furnished a way for its closing, the cat would be almost blind in the sunlight. Look at a cat's eyes in bright daylight. The pupil has closed, or contracted, to a narrow line.

Other animals of the cat family have eyes with pupils that contract in the same way. The fox, a night hunter of the dog family, also has such eyes. So do some crawling creatures, such as the alligator.

The owl is also a night hunter. His eyes, for that reason, are very large and are made so that they gather in more light than those of other birds. But the pupils do not contract in the day-time, as the cat's do. So the owl goes into some dark spot at sunrise and waits for the darkness of the next night when he can see to capture his food.

The owl feeds on mice and other small animals that seek food in the darkness. He flies noiselessly through the night, peering into every hiding place, much as the fox does. So he must have eyes in front in order to see and catch his food.

Eyes in the Sky

Hawks, eagles, and some other birds are also hunters, but they hunt by day. The daytime hunting birds sight their food from on high and must be able to see at great distances.

The eagle, that you may have seen swinging in great wide circles, high in the sky, is able to see far beneath him the chicken or squirrel that is to serve him as a meal. He can see small objects which no man could see without powerful field glasses.

The eagle can see objects beneath him much better than can most birds because of the heavy ridges over his eyes. Eyes used in looking long distances need a shade. This is furnished by the overhanging ridges, much as a person shades his eyes with his hand when looking at things far away.

Another interesting thing about the eagle's eye is a third lid, which passes over the eyeball with a shutter movement. This lid clears dust from the surface of the eye and yet does not keep the eagle from seeing, because it is transparent.

All birds, such as the robin or oriole or hawk, have this third transparent lid. It is so thin and moves so fast that it is hardly ever seen, even by men who study birds closely.

Upward-Looking Eyes

Instead of looking down, like the eagle, the frog must look upward. His eyes must serve to protect him. The frog is not a hunter, but a hunted animal. Danger to him is likely to come from above.

The frog spends much of his time in the water with nothing showing above the surface but his eyes, which look very much like bubbles. He is well hidden from his enemies and is not easily surprised. His bubble eyes are unusually quick, and are his greatest protection against the many birds, such as owls and hawks, that attack him.

Other animals that spend much time in the water have the same upward-looking eyes. Among them is the savage alligator. He also passes long hours lying half in the water along the edge of a stream. All the time the alligator is able to keep a sharp watch around him with his eyes that stick out above the surface.

Insects' Eyes

You know that a housefly can easily escape a sudden blow. You have only to look at his eyes to understand why. They are large, covering most of his head, and are so made that he can see in all directions. Each eye has many parts, and each tiny part is a separate eye. The two large eyes of the fly are really clusters of many eyes.

Men have counted the eyes in these clusters and discovered that there are 8000 of these separate eyes, each one pointed in a different direction. It is small wonder that the fly easily escapes when you try to hit him.

Eyes such as the fly's are called compound eyes. Many insects have compound eyes, and some of them are even more wonderful than the eyes of the housefly. The dragonfly has about 13,000 separate eyes in its clusters.

These insects with compound eyes cannot roll their eyes or turn their heads, but they have little need to do so with such a battery of eyes to use.

Snakes' Eyes

Instead of the usual protection of eyelids the snake has a transparent, horny plate, like a window, fastened to his skin. This plate makes a wonderful protection for the eyes of an animal that spends his life crawling on the ground, where dirt, sticks, or other objects could easily enter the eye.

This transparent plate goes with the skin when the snake sheds it. Eyelids such as we have would be hard to shed, but the snake's eye plate gives little trouble.

Shortly before the snake loses his old skin, a milky fluid begins to form under the plate. In time this fluid hardens into a new transparent plate, just like the one which is being lost. But before the fluid becomes hard, it is not clear, and so the snake is almost blind.

During this time the snake is unusually savage, because he is fearful. He will strike at anything near by.

384

Fishes' Eyes

The round unblinking eyes of a fish, with their enormous pupils, seem strange until we remember that the fish's home is the water. It is very different from our home, the air.

We sometimes need to blink or close our eyelids to protect our eyes from dust and light and blows. The fish has no need of the eyelid. There is no dust in the water, and the water itself forms a great cushion, which protects the eyes of the fish from accidents. Anyone who has tried to slap hands under water knows how the water acts as a cushion.

The light under the water is very dim, even on the brightest days. The pupil of the fish's eye must be large in order to gather in as much light as possible.

The fish, like all other animals, has eyes exactly suited to its way of living.

Mary Bowen Stephenson

Vegetables

A carrot has a green fringed top;
  A beet is royal red;
And lettuces are curious
  All curled and run to head.

Some beans have strings to tie them on,
  And, what is still more queer,
Ripe corn is nothing more or less
  Than one enormous ear!

But when potatoes all have eyes,
  Why is it they should be
Put in the ground and covered up—
  Where it's too dark to see?

Rachel Field

Fun and Nonsense

Kasha—The Story of a Cow

Kasha was a cow.

But Kasha was not just any cow. Kasha was a very beautiful cow. Her hide was black and white. Her eyes were dark and dreamy. And her horns were curled just so.

But because Kasha was a very beautiful cow, she was also a very spoiled cow. If she couldn't have her own way, she would shake her beautiful horns as if to say, "Let me or else—."

Kasha belonged to Ronka and his wife Ninya. They were Russian country people, and they lived near the Black Sea. They both loved Kasha very much. It was Ninya who milked her.

Every morning Ninya in her clumsy shoes would clump over the board walk to the cow stall. Behind her clumped Ronka in his stout high boots, always carrying some pieces of dried pears in his pocket.

The pears were Kasha's favorite food. While Ninya sat milking, Ronka would stand patting Kasha's black head. At the same time Kasha would slowly chew up her dried pears.

388

After Ninya was through milking, Ronka, with one arm around Kasha's big neck, would take her out of the stall to the bright green grass under the big pear tree. Here Kasha stayed all day. She grazed contentedly, and sometimes she drank from a wooden water tub.

Kasha wasn't tied with a rope. The only thing she would stand for around her beautiful black neck was Ronka's arm. But she never ran away, for she had everything she wanted. She was not only a beautiful cow and a spoiled cow but also a very happy cow, the happiest cow in all Russia.

One day soon after Easter, when Ronka came home from the village, he called into the kitchen from outside, "Ninya, Ninya, I see you are making bread. But come listen to me. There's going to be a party in the village this afternoon. There will be musicians and dancing and a puppet show. Get yourself ready and we'll go."

But Ninya was annoyed this morning. Her face was red and hot. She had burned her finger when taking some bread out of the oven. She clumped to the kitchen door to look out at Ronka. He was at the well, splashing water all over his face, for he was hot from his walk to the village.

"Such nonsense!" Ninya said shortly. "You know very well that you have work to do, and I have my house to clean. We are too busy to go to the village this afternoon."

Ronka rubbed his face still harder and splashed some water behind his ears. Then he said, "Oh, never mind cleaning the house. Put on your pretty red skirt and embroidered blouse, and we'll have some fun today."

"No, I can't go!" said Ninya. Before she could say more, she smelled something. "Oh, oh, my bread!" she cried. "It's all your fault, you good-for-nothing, lazy man. I'll make you eat it!" She was almost in tears, she was so annoyed.

Out of the oven she took a pan of black, smoking bread and slammed the oven door. Now Ninya was really crying.

Ronka stood outside the door of the cottage. He didn't like to see his Ninya crying, but he was too timid to go in.

"Ninya," he begged anxiously, "let's go to the party."

Ninya would not answer. He tried again.

"Ninya, the red skirt and embroidered blouse are so pretty on you."

Ninya looked up and dried the tears on her red face, but said not a word.

Ronka tried a third time.

"Ninya, I'll dump out the burned bread. I'll feed the chickens. I'll put water in Kasha's tub. I'll do all these things for you, if you'll go with me to the party."

Ninya smiled just a little. Then she said, "Yes, yes, I'll go." She untied her apron and threw it into a corner. She clumped to the dresser to get her best clothes.

Ronka was so happy that he and Ninya were to go to the party that he took the black, burned bread out right away. From outside he called, "Hurry, Ninya, hurry. We must get to the party before they close the gate of the inn."

When Ronka came back, Ninya, in her red skirt and pretty blouse and bright kerchief, was ready to go. Ronka put on a pointed cap, a shirt embroidered like Ninya's blouse, and a short jacket. Then off they hurried. Ronka in his stout boots and Ninya in her big clumsy shoes clumped happily away to the village.

Kasha was grazing behind the pear tree and so did not see her Ronka and her Ninya hurrying to the village. She was too busy being happy and beautiful and spoiled. After a while she lay down under the pear tree to chew her cud. She lay there for one hour—two hours—three hours—and another half hour.

Then she rose and, with a shake of her curled horns, she walked around the pear tree, straight to her wooden water tub. Kasha always drank water after chewing her cud for exactly three and one-half hours. She was that spoiled!

But today, though Kasha licked the bottom of the tub, she could not get even one drop of water. Ronka had forgotten to fill it. He had been too busy thinking about the good time Ninya and he were going to have.

Just to make sure, Kasha shook the tub from side to side with her horns. But there was no water, and Kasha was very thirsty.

When she lifted her head, the tub came with it. Perched on her beautiful horns, it formed a fine hat. Perhaps this is just what Kasha wanted, for she headed straight for the cottage. Did she want to show Ninya and Ronka that she needed water?

The kitchen door stood wide open. So Kasha stuck her beautiful head and the tub inside.

"Moo, moo," she said.

393

No answer.

Kasha stepped a little way in. "Moo, moo-oo."

No answer.

Kasha stepped halfway in. "Moo, moo-oo-oo!"

Still no answer.

Kasha stepped all the way into the kitchen. There was no Ronka there. There was no Ninya there. There was no one there.

But Kasha was still very thirsty.

Her four feet clumped down hard on the floor. Clump, clump! The tub on her head bumped into a cupboard. Two dishes came crashing down to break into a hundred pieces on the floor. One back leg hit the kitchen table, and down went a bowl, spilling flour all over the floor.

From the kitchen Kasha clumped into the front room. The tub on her head banged into the clock. Down it came crashing to the floor, and a metal tray with it. Kasha switched her tail, and a cushion rolled out of a chair.

394

By this time Kasha was very tired. She forgot
that she was beautiful. She forgot that she was
spoiled. She forgot that she was happy. She even
forgot that she was thirsty. She just knew that
she was tired. So Kasha got down on her knees.
Then she went all the way down, full length, on
Ronka's and Ninya's front-room rug between the
clock and the cushion.

With the tub still on her horns, Kasha was
lying on the front-room rug, chewing her cud,
when Ronka and Ninya clumped home from the
party.

"Look!" said Ninya, blinking her eyes to make
sure she was seeing right.

"I'm looking," said Ronka.

"Now, how did she get in?" asked Ninya, much
annoyed.

"We must have rushed off and left the kitchen
door open," said Ronka.

"Well, don't just stand there. Do something," said Ninya, picking up the precious clock and looking at the spots on the rug.

"What shall I do?" asked Ronka timidly.

Just then Kasha decided to get to her feet. The wooden tub came loose from her beautiful horns and thumped to the floor. Ronka ran to put his arm around Kasha's neck.

"Kasha," he said, "I'm sorry I forgot. Come, I'll put water in your tub right now. Then I'll give you some dried pears while Ninya milks you."

So off the three of them clumped. First they went to put water in the wooden tub. Kasha drank and drank and drank. She drank two tubfuls. She was just that thirsty!

Then Ronka turned Kasha toward the cow stall. And while Ninya sat milking Kasha, Ronka stood patting Kasha's black head, and Kasha chewed slowly on her dried pears.

Now Kasha felt right again. She was not only the most beautiful cow in all Russia but also a very spoiled cow. And just like you or me, Kasha enjoyed being spoiled.

Susanna Wolfenden

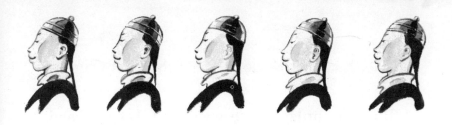

The Five Chinese Brothers

Once upon a time there were Five Chinese Brothers, and they all looked just alike. They lived with their mother in a little house not far from the sea.

The First Chinese Brother could swallow the sea. The Second Chinese Brother had an iron neck. The Third Chinese Brother could stretch and stretch and stretch his legs. The Fourth Chinese Brother could not be burned. And the Fifth Chinese Brother could hold his breath for as long as he wished.

Every morning the First Chinese Brother would go fishing. And whatever the weather, he would come back to the village with beautiful fish which he had caught and could sell at the market for a very good price.

One day, as he was leaving the market place, a little boy stopped him and asked if he might go fishing with him.

"No, it cannot be done," said the First Chinese Brother.

But the little boy begged and begged, and finally the First Chinese Brother said, "You may go if you will promise one thing. Promise to obey me promptly."

"Yes, yes," the little boy promised.

Early next morning the First Chinese Brother and the little boy went down to the beach.

"Remember," said the First Chinese Brother, "you must obey me promptly. When I make a sign for you to come back, you must come at once."

"Yes, yes," the little boy promised.

Then the First Chinese Brother swallowed the sea. And all the fish were left high and dry at the bottom of the sea. And all the treasures of the sea lay uncovered.

The little boy was delighted. He ran here and there, filling his pockets with strange pebbles, wonderful shells, and queer plants which he had never seen before.

Near the shore the First Chinese Brother gathered some fish while he kept holding the sea in his mouth. Soon he grew tired. It is very hard to hold the sea. So he made a sign with his hand for the little boy to come back. The little boy saw him, but he paid no attention.

The First Chinese Brother made movements with his arms that meant "Come back!"

But did the little boy care? Not a bit, and he ran farther away.

Then the First Chinese Brother felt the sea pushing up inside him. Bubbles came out of his mouth. He waved as hard as he could to call the little boy back. But the little boy made faces at him and ran as fast as he could the other way.

The First Chinese Brother held the sea until he thought he could stand it no longer. All of a sudden the sea pushed its way out of his mouth and went back to its bed—and the little boy vanished.

When the First Chinese Brother returned to the village alone, he was taken by the police. He was tried and told he was going to have his head cut off.

On the morning he was to die, he said to the judge: "Your Honor, will you allow me to go and bid my mother good-by?"

"It is only fair," said the judge.

So the First Chinese Brother went home—and the Second Chinese Brother came back in his place.

All the people were gathered on the village square to see him killed. The man who was to kill him took a sword and hit him a mighty blow on the neck.

But the Second Chinese Brother got up and smiled.

He was the one with the iron neck, and the sharpest sword just could not cut his head off.

400

Everybody was angry, and they decided that he should be drowned.

On the morning he was to die, the Second Chinese Brother said to the judge: "Your Honor, will you allow me to go and bid my mother good-by?"

"It is only fair," said the judge.

So the Second Chinese Brother went home, and the Third Chinese Brother came back in his place.

He was pushed on a boat, which made for the open sea. When they were far out on the ocean, the Third Chinese Brother was thrown overboard. But he began to stretch and stretch his legs full length, way down to the bottom of the sea, and all the time his smiling face was bobbing up and down on the waves. He just could not be drowned.

Everybody was very angry, and they all decided that he should be burned.

On the morning he was to die, the Third Chinese Brother said to the judge: "Your Honor, will you allow me to go and bid my mother good-by?"

"It is only fair," said the judge.

So the Third Chinese Brother went home, and the Fourth Chinese Brother came back in his place.

He was tied to a big pole. Fire was set to it, and all the people stood around watching. From the middle of the flames they heard him say, "This is quite pleasant."

"Bring some more wood!" the people cried.

The fire roared higher.

"Now it is quite comfortable," said the Fourth Chinese Brother, for he was the one who could not be burned.

Everybody was getting more and more angry, and they all decided he should be smothered.

On the morning he was to die, the Fourth Chinese Brother said to the judge: "Your Honor, will you allow me to go and bid my mother good-by?"

402

"It is only fair," said the judge.

So the Fourth Chinese Brother went home, and the Fifth Chinese Brother came back in his place.

A large brick oven had been built on the village square, and it had been all filled with whipped cream. The Fifth Chinese Brother was shoveled into the oven, right in the middle of the whipped cream. The door was shut tight, and everybody sat around and waited for him to smother.

They were not going to be tricked again! So they stayed there all night and even a little after dawn, just to make sure.

Then they opened the door and pulled him out. And he shook the whipped cream off himself and said, "My! That was a good sleep!"

Everybody stared with open mouth and round eyes. But the judge stepped up and said, "We have tried to kill you in every possible way. We have tried to cut your head off, to drown you, to burn you, and to smother you. Somehow it can't be done. It must be that you did nothing wrong, and therefore should not be killed."

"Yes, yes," shouted all the people. So they let him go and he went home.

And the Five Chinese Brothers and their mother all lived together happily for many years.

Claire Huchet Bishop
Kurt Wiese

Master of All Masters

There was once a girl who went to the fair to hire herself out as a servant. Soon an old man in green pantaloons came up to her and said he would like to hire her to work at his house.

"Very well," said the girl, and the two started toward his home.

"Now at my house," the old man said as they went along, "we have our own names for things. You must always call me Master of All Masters."

"Yes, Master of All Masters," answered the girl.

When they got inside the little house, the old man pointed to a bed that stood in the corner near the fireplace, and he asked, "Now what would you call that?"

"Why, bed or bunk or whatever you please, sir," said the girl.

"No," said the man. "That is my barnacle, and you must always call it that."

"Barnacle it shall be, sir," answered the girl.

Then the man pointed to some pantaloons hanging on a peg and asked, "What would you call those?"

"Why," said the girl, "pantaloons or trousers or whatever you please, sir."

"Wrong," answered the man. "Those are my squibs and crackers, and you must always call them that."

"Squibs and crackers they shall be, sir," said the girl.

Then the man pointed to the cat sitting beside the fire, and he asked, "Now what would you call her?"

"Well," said the girl, "cat or pussy or whatever you please, sir."

"Wrong again," said the man. "That is White-face Siminy, and you must always call her that."

"White-face Siminy she shall be, sir," the girl answered.

Then the man pointed to the fire in the fire-place and said, "Now what would you call that?"

"Fire or flame or whatever you please, sir," said the girl.

"No," the man answered. "That is hot cockalorum, and you must always call it that."

"Hot cockalorum it shall be, sir," said the girl.

Then the man pointed to a bucket of water that sat on a stool near the door. "Now what would you call that?" he asked.

The poor girl by that time was much upset. She answered hopelessly, "Why, water or wet or whatever you please, sir."

"That," said the man, "is pondalorum, and you must always call it that."

"Pondalorum it shall be, sir," said the girl.

Then the man, waving his arm to show he meant the whole house from chimney to cellar, asked, "What would you call all this?"

"Well, house or cottage or whatever you please, sir," said the girl.

"No," he answered. "This is high topper mountain, and you must always call it that."

"High topper mountain it shall be, sir," she said, wishing she had never been hired.

That night when all the house was still, the girl leaped from her bed, stuck her head out of her bedroom door, and shouted, "Master of All Masters, get out of your barnacle and put on your squibs and crackers! White-face Siminy has a spot of hot cockalorum on the end of her tail, and unless you put on some pondalorum, high topper mountain will be all on hot cockalorum. That's all!"

An English Folk Tale

Eletelephony

Once there was an elephant,
Who tried to use the telephant—
No! no! I mean an elephone
Who tried to use the telephone—
(Dear me! I am not certain quite
That even now I've got it right.)
Howe'er it was, he got his trunk
Entangled in the telephunk;
The more he tried to get it free,
The louder buzzed the telephee—
(I fear I'd better drop the song
Of elephop and telephong!)

Laura E. Richards

Mister Penny

In the Neighbor's Garden

Once there was an old man. His name was Mister Penny. He lived in a wreck of a shed by a path to the village of Wuddle. He was too poor to have anything else to live in.

Although Mister Penny worked year after year in the factory of Wuddle, he spent all his money buying food for his family of animals. He had a horse and a cow and a goat and a pig and a lamb and a hen and a rooster.

They were all lazy, and Mister Penny had to work very hard to feed them. They would do nothing for themselves. And Doody, the rooster, even got into trouble whenever he could. He was really very bad.

Every morning before the sun, Mister Penny was up cleaning the shed and getting breakfast for his animals. When everything was ready, he'd say good-by and tell each one to be good—each one but Doody. When he came to Doody, he'd say, "Please try to be good, Doody. You can try to be good, can't you?"

410

Trudging along the path that wound across the fields, he would say to himself, "It's hard for an old man like me to work in a factory. But I'm glad I have a job, that I am. How else would I keep my large family?"

One morning in June after Mister Penny had gone to his work, Doody started crowing. Then he flew to the shed roof and strutted along the edge.

"Cock-a-doodle-do," he crowed. "I can see farther than any of you!"

"Well, if you can see so much," said Splop, the goat, "tell us what's growing in the neighbor's garden."

Then all the others listened, for Doody began naming everything he saw that was good to eat. And he named some things he didn't see, too.

"Mmmmmm," said Mooloo, the cow. "That's the kind of food I like."

"Too bad it belongs to somebody else," said Limpy, the horse.

"Oh, why worry?" said Splop. "It belongs to that selfish old man from the city. He'd never see us. His house is far away over the hill, and he keeps his watchdog chained up."

When Doody heard that, he flapped his wings. The next minute he was flying over the fence.

"Come back," squawked the hen, running after him. "You'd better come back!" But when she reached the fence, she too flapped her wings and flew over.

"Those chickens think they're something because they have wings," said Splop. And off she raced toward the gate.

Now the gate was broken and sagging and never closed quite tight. Splop promptly pushed her nose through the hole and twisted and turned and butted and bumped. At last the gate opened, and out she went. Then after her went Limpy and Mooloo and Mimkin, the lamb.

But not Pugwug, the pig! He had been in such a hurry that he had tried to push through a hole under the fence.

"Wait for me," he cried. "Wait for me!"

But nobody heard Pugwug. They were already in the neighbor's garden. First they found red strawberries and ate them all up, even the leaves and the blossoms. Then they ate what they wanted of the young cabbages and carrots.

Pretty soon they discovered some little green pumpkins in the cornfield. But the little pumpkins were too hard to bite. So they rolled them around like balls.

"Mmm," said Mooloo when she had eaten so many young cornstalks she didn't seem to care for any more. She went over to Limpy, who was near the apple trees. "What's the matter?" she asked, for Limpy had stopped chewing apples and stood with his ears straight up, listening hard.

"What's the matter?" Mooloo asked again.

413

Limpy didn't answer. He lifted his head still higher and looked back over the hill. And there it was—the dog he had heard! And behind the dog came the neighbor himself with a whip.

"Run!" Limpy shouted. "Run!"

Chukluk, the hen, started running in circles. "Oh, he'll catch us! Catch us! Catch us!" she squawked. But soon she found the fence and flew home safely.

The others all ran through the gate—all but Doody. Doody stayed where he was until the dog could see him. Then he arched his tail and strutted.

"Just wait till I catch you," growled the dog. And on he came after the rooster.

Doody laughed and crowed as he ran along the bushes by the fence. And even when it was time to fly over, he stopped and strutted and crowed back, "Catch me, old Big Teeth! Why don't you catch me?"

That made the dog so angry that he jumped straight into the air. And he did catch Doody. He caught him by the tail.

For a second the rooster thought he had come to his end. But then he started flapping his wings and pulling. He pulled till his tail came loose. And the next thing he knew, he was over the fence, but he had no arching tail left at all! He ran for the shed to hide in the straw.

But the others had no time to watch Doody. The neighbor was there at the gate with his whip. He was pushing and pounding. All at once an old board broke in two, and in came his head through the hole.

"If he comes any farther I'll butt him!" said Splop.

When the neighbor saw Splop coming toward him with her head down, ready to butt, he decided he did not want to get in after all.

"I'll come back when the old man's home," he growled. And off he went up the hill.

Trouble for Everybody

Then Mimkin began to cry.

"Don't cry now," said Limpy. "He's gone."

"But my stomach!" said Mimkin. "It aches!"

"Mine too-oo!" cried Mooloo.

Then Limpy began to feel such pains from green apples that he couldn't talk. He went off to his bed in the straw, and the others all followed. On their way to the shed Splop saw the tail end of Pugwug under the fence. That poor pig was still stuck fast!

416

Splop laughed even though her stomach ached. Then she and Chukluk ran to help Pugwug. They pawed and scratched away dirt until he had room to wiggle out. Pugwug was so tired from squealing and grunting that he just followed the others to the shed and was soon fast asleep on the floor.

"What's this, what's this?" said Mister Penny when he opened his gate that evening. "Not one of my family to meet me?"

When he came into the shed and saw them looking so sad, he did not know what to think.

He dropped his dinner pail and ran to look at Limpy's tongue. Then he ran to Mooloo. Her tongue hung down like a piece of wet cloth.

"They're all sick!" said Mister Penny. He took a big bottle and a tablespoon from the cupboard and started giving them sticky medicine.

R8

Pugwug got some, too, though he kicked and cried. He had no aches or pains and he didn't want medicine. He wanted something to eat!

Last of all Mister Penny came to Doody. He picked him up from the straw to pour his medicine in. "What's this?" he exclaimed. "What has happened to you?"

Then he looked all over the floor, but he could see no sign of a tail at all.

What could have happened? All sick at once, and no tail on the rooster! He put Doody in the old wheelbarrow and covered him up with straw, because he thought he might feel cold. Then he tried to think of something else he could do.

"They'll feel better if they can sleep," he said. So he brought them fresh straw to rest on.

Then he took the lantern and tiptoed off to his end of the shed. After a little he brought out some bread and cheese for his supper. But he didn't seem to feel hungry. So he put it away again and took up the evening paper.

He was reading the funny pictures when there came a loud knock on his door. "My eyes!" he exclaimed, jumping up to open it. "Who can it be?"

418

Now Limpy had heard, too. He got up and stuck his head through a hole in the wall.

In came the big neighbor, waving his whip and shouting at the top of his voice.

"Whatever is the matter with him?" thought Mister Penny.

The man's words were popping out like popcorn over a hot fire, and Mister Penny could understand only a few of them. "No tops . . . carrots! New plants . . . the ground! Seeds scratched up! Every apple . . . bite in it!"

"It's his garden," thought Mister Penny. "Something's happened to his garden."

Then shivers ran up his back, for he caught the words "hungry pests . . . good-for-nothing creatures!"

419

"So that's what made them all sick!" Mister Penny shook his head. "Oh me, oh me."

"But it's really my fault," he said quickly. "I knew the gate needed mending. The worst of it is I have no money to pay for the damage."

"You'd just better do away with those pests," growled the neighbor. "I'll take them myself in pay for their damage—though they're not much good. I suppose the pig might give good meat, and the lamb might make good stew."

"Oh, please!" said Mister Penny. "Not that!"

"Well," growled the neighbor, "I'm behind with my work. If you must keep those pests, here's what you can do. Plow the three south fields before the new moon. Clean out the stones from that pasture land near my pine woods. Cut the grass on my lawn. And then you can furnish me with milk for the rest of the summer."

He slapped a paper on the table. "It's all listed there. Decide overnight which you'll do—give me your hungry beasts, or do this work."

When the neighbor had gone, Mister Penny sat down by his table. "Oh, me!" he said to himself. "Is there nothing I can do to save my family?"

Limpy Has an Idea

Now Limpy, who had been watching and listening, went over to Mooloo and woke her up. When she heard the story, she almost cried.

"We've got to do something!" said Limpy.

"But what can we do?" asked Mooloo.

"Well," said Limpy, "I'm not so lame as I've made believe. I can do that plowing as well as any other horse. And there's a collar on that old plow in the corner. I'm going to do the plowing!"

"You know," said Mooloo, "I've been giving only about a cupful of milk. I was too lazy to chew my cud, that's why. But I'll chew my cud thirty hours a day before I'll let that mean man take any of us!"

"What's the matter?" crowed Doody.

"Hush!" said Limpy. "People will think it's time to get up before they've gone to bed."

Then Splop came tumbling over to see what had happened. She was so noisy about it that she woke up Mimkin and Chukluk. But not Pugwug! That pig could sleep through anything.

"Say!" said Splop. "If that old Thunderstorm ever tries to take me away from Mister Penny, I'll butt him so high that he'll never come down."

"Don't talk nonsense," said Limpy. "We damaged his garden and we have to pay. What work do you choose?"

"I don't choose any!" said Splop. "But if it has to be done, I'll clean out those old stones."

"I'll clip the lawn," said Mimkin.

"I'll eat that bitter feed so that I can lay bigger eggs and more of them," said Chukluk.

Splop shook her horns in front of Doody. "What good is a rooster without any tail?" she teased. "All he can do is eat bugs."

That gave Limpy an idea. Doody could follow the plow and save all the worms. Mister Penny never had enough worms at his stand outside the fence for the men who came from the city to fish.

422

"Well, come on!" said Splop. "Let's go!"

Limpy looked through the hole. Mister Penny had fallen asleep with his head on the table.

Limpy looked out of the window. Everything was black. So then he let Splop run ahead to open the gate, and forgetting he'd ever felt lame, Limpy hurried to get the plow. He pushed his head through the collar.

"Oh, I almost forgot!" he said. He went over to Pugwug and woke him up. "I need something heavy to hold the plow down. Come!"

And out they went into the dark—all but Mooloo and Chukluk, who stayed behind, one to chew her cud and the other to eat her feed.

All through the night Mister Penny sat by his table and painfully tried to think. Whenever he fell asleep, his dreams woke him up.

When morning came, he still didn't know how to save his animals. He went back to look at them.

"All sleeping except Mooloo and the chickens," he said to himself. "But they don't act sick. They must be feeling better."

He put his stool down beside Mooloo and started to milk.

"Mooloo!" cried Mister Penny after a few minutes. Instead of a cupful of milk, there was a pailful! He jumped up and threw his arms around Mooloo's neck. "Good Mooloo! If you only knew how much I need this milk! I'll take my neighbor more than he said. And there's plenty for me and some to sell besides."

The chickens were squawking and crowing, trying to make him look. He went to see if by chance Chukluk had laid an egg. Stooping down, he looked closely at something in the straw.

An egg as large as a goose could lay! And a canful of beautiful worms!

424

Mister Penny picked up one chicken under each arm and danced around. He hugged them so hard that they squawked to get down.

Mister Penny cooked the egg to put in his dinner pail. Then he ran out and put the worms on his stand, where he sold them like newspapers. They were two for a penny or five cents a dozen, and he left a box on the stand for the money.

Next he put part of the milk into his newest tin pail and went up the hill to deliver it to his neighbor. When he knocked timidly at the back door, the neighbor came out and said, "Well, old man, I see you have a lot done already! If you work as fast every night as you did last night, you'll have it all done before the new moon."

Mister Penny looked around to see what the man was talking about.

The grass on the lawn was clipped short. A big pile of stones had been cleaned out from the pasture land. And in the fields was a long stretch of newly plowed earth.

"He must think I did it!" thought Mister Penny. But before he could open his mouth, the neighbor had gone in and shut the door.

425

"Do I dare knock again to tell him?" said Mister Penny to himself. He stood there trying to decide. Then came the first shriek of the factory whistle. "No," he said. "I'll go to my job. I can keep my family one day more!"

"I can't understand it at all!" he kept saying to himself as he trudged across the fields. "Somebody's been doing that work. But only goblins and witches and fairies do their work in the night when no one can see. And the milk! And that egg! And where under the sun did those worms come from? But surely I'm not dreaming. I'm awake or I wouldn't be sniffing the flowers and feeling a stone in my shoe."

The next morning everything happened just as it had the day before. More milk! Another giant egg! A canful of beautiful worms! And two times as much work done at the neighbor's!

"Well, old man," said the neighbor as he took the milk, "you worked faster last night than before. You'll have the damage paid for before the new moon."

And again, before Mister Penny could open his mouth, the neighbor shut the door.

426

"Well, I'm jigsawed to a puzzle!" said Mister Penny, as he trudged off to his job in the factory of Wuddle. "Jigsawed to a puzzle! It must be the goblins and witches and fairies who are helping me out—though I never believed in them before. Goblins and witches and fairies and things!"

A New Idea

On the first night of the new moon Mister Penny's animals came tumbling home all out of breath. They woke up Mooloo. They woke up the hen. "Hooray! Hooray! It's all done. The damage is paid for. It's finished!"

"And what now?" said Splop, kicking her legs and shaking her head. "I like to work!"

"Me too," said Mimkin, the lamb.

"And me!" said Doody.

"And me," said Pugwug. "I like to ride on that plow."

Limpy dragged the plow to its place in the corner. "You know," he said, "I've been thinking all the while I've been plowing. What stupid creatures we've been—never doing any work! Now that we've tried it, we all like to work. And all this time we might have had a garden right here—for ourselves and Mister Penny."

"Ooooh!" said Splop. "We'd better get started. This field is more stones than dirt."

But Limpy made them all hurry to bed, because it was almost time for Mister Penny to get up. Tomorrow night they could start their own garden.

On Monday morning when Mister Penny came out of his shed, his pipe dropped from his mouth. There at one end of his own field the ground had been plowed and piles of stones cleaned out!

"Well, I'm jigsawed to a puzzle! Those good creatures!" he said. "They did all that work for my neighbor, and now they're starting a garden for me. A garden for me and my animals!"

And Mister Penny just stood there staring until the shriek of the factory whistle made him jump.

As he hurried across the fields, he laughed to himself and talked back to the birds and crickets.

428

"A garden for me and my animals—and for the hummingbirds and the crickets too!" said Mister Penny. "Sunflowers in it—and squash—"

On Saturday noon Mister Penny hurried home from the factory. He took all the pennies he'd saved from selling worms and milk—a whole bagful of pennies—and he and his family went to market to buy seeds.

First they bought seeds for carrots and lettuce and all the things they liked to eat—except horse-radish. They decided not to plant that, because you can't make a good meal out of horse-radish even when you're hungry. Then they hurried home, and Mister Penny planted everything in the nice, soft dirt. Only no horse-radish!

The rains came and the sun was warm. Before very long Mister Penny's garden was the most beautiful garden in the town of Wuddle. But Mister Penny still thought it was goblins and witches and fairies who were helping him.

Then one night there came a storm. The thunder and lightning got him up. He went out to see if his garden was all right. He thought he saw something moving.

Mister Penny set his lantern down behind him and looked again.

"Those good creatures!" he said to himself. "They shouldn't be out in such weather. If they're not afraid, I'll take them inside for hot tea so they won't catch cold."

He went very, very slowly toward the biggest thing he saw moving. "Don't be afraid," he said. "It's only Mister Penny."

But just as he reached it, there came a flash of lightning as bright as day.

"Well, what on earth?" he exclaimed, for as sure as breathing, the big black thing was lame Limpy, no longer lame, pulling the plow with Pugwug serving as a weight to hold it down. And behind walked Doody looking for worms. And a little farther over was Splop cleaning out stones. And Mimkin clipping grass!

Mister Penny dropped his umbrella and ran around in the rain, patting each one.

"So you are the goblins and witches and fairies and things!" He chuckled. "Oh, my good beasts, with such a garden we'll have more than plenty to eat, and I'll no longer need to work in that noisy factory of Wuddle! I can stay right at home and just work in my garden!"

So Mister Penny kept on selling worms and milk, and then he sold truckloads of stones for filling up holes in the road. And soon he had enough money to buy lumber and nails and paint.

Then he built a new house in the middle of his garden—a long pink house with seven doors in a row. On the top he put a little windmill for the winds to play with, and a little house for the birds. And near some bushes in the yard he laid an old board for the crickets to hide under.

And in the long summer evenings the people of Wuddle would look over the low fence and say to each other, "Isn't he a queer one, living in a house with all those animals! But I say, they're the happiest family in Wuddle."

Marie Hall Ets

431

The Four Presents

I had four brothers over the sea,
   Perrie, Merrie, Dixi, Domine;
And they each sent a present unto me.
   Petrum, Partrum, Paradisi Tempore,
   Perrie, Merrie, Dixi, Domine.

The first sent a goose without a bone,
   Perrie, Merrie, Dixi, Domine;
The second sent a cherry without a stone,
   Petrum, Partrum, Paradisi Tempore,
   Perrie, Merrie, Dixi, Domine.

The third sent a blanket without a thread,
   Perrie, Merrie, Dixi, Domine;
The fourth sent a book no man could read,
   Petrum, Partrum, Paradisi Tempore,
   Perrie, Merrie, Dixi, Domine.

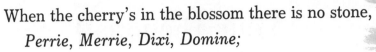

When the cherry's in the blossom there is no stone,
    Perrie, Merrie, Dixi, Domine;
When the goose is in the egg-shell, there is no bone,
    Petrum, Partrum, Paradisi Tempore,
    Perrie, Merrie, Dixi, Domine.

When the wool's on the sheep's back there is no
    thread,
    Perrie, Merrie, Dixi, Domine;
When the book's in the press, no man it can read,
    Petrum, Partrum, Paradisi Tempore,
    Perrie, Merrie, Dixi, Domine.

An Old English Riddle

433

Your Dictionary

The little dictionary, or glossary, on the following pages will help you to pronounce and to understand the meanings of hard words in this book.

The pronunciation of each word is shown by division into syllables, by an accent mark (if it has more than one syllable), by marks over the vowels, and by respelling, if necessary, to give correct sounds.

The list below shows you how each marked vowel is pronounced. The word after each letter is a common word which you know how to pronounce. It tells you the sound of a vowel when it is marked in the same way. This is called a pronunciation key.

ā	lāte	ī	hīde	ū	ūse
ă	ăm	ĭ	hĭd	ŭ	ŭs
ä	färm			û	bûrn
ȧ	ȧsk	ō	ōld		
â	câre	ŏ	nŏt	o͞o	mo͞on
		ô	hôrse	o͝o	fo͝ot
ē	wē	ȯ	sȯft	oi	oil
ĕ	wĕt			ou	out
ê	lettêr				

A

a ban'don (ȧ băn'dŭn). To leave behind; to give up completely.

Abd el Ka ru'zeh (äbd ĕl kȧ ro͞o' zĕ).

ache (āk). 1. To have pain. 2. A pain that continues.

a'cre (ā'kêr). A piece of land about 5000 square yards in size.

a diós' (ä dyōs'). Spanish word for *good-by*.

Af'ri ca (ăf'rĭ kȧ). A continent south of Europe.

Aire'dale (âr'dāl). A large dog, black and tan in color, with short, stiff hair. It is a kind of terrier.

aisle (īl). A long passage between rows of seats.

Al'ba ny (ôl'bȧ nĭ). The capital of the state of New York.

al'li ga tor (ăl'ĭ gā têr). A large, crawling animal with a huge mouth, long tail, and hard plated skin. It lives in rivers in warm countries.

an'chor (ăng'kêr). 1. To hold fast by means of a heavy weight. 2. A heavy piece of iron or steel with hooks and a

434

crossbar. It is used to hold a ship in place.

anx'ious (ăngk'shŭs). 1. Worried or fearful. 2. Eager.

arch (ärch). 1. To bend like an arch. 2. An opening, such as a doorway, with a curved top.

Ar i zo'na (ăr ĭ zō'nȧ). A state in the southwest part of the United States.

Ar'pad (är'pȧd).

as ton'ish (ȧs tŏn'ĭsh). To surprise greatly.

A the'na (ȧ thē'nȧ). A Greek goddess. She was wise and just, and protected people who were in the right. She could hurl thunderbolts, but was interested in the arts and in learning.

Au'no (ou'nō).

Aus tral'ia (ôs trāl'yȧ). An island continent in the South Pacific Ocean.

az'ure (ăzh'ẽr). A blue color like that of a clear sky.

B

bail (bāl). 1. To dip and throw out water from something. 2. The handle of a pail.

ban'dit (băn'dĭt). A lawless person who robs others, especially travelers.

ba'o bab (bā'ō băb). A very large tree in Africa. Its fruit is good to eat and is sometimes called monkey bread.

bar'na cle (bär'nȧ k'l). 1. Master of All Masters' name for a bed. 2. A little, hard-shelled sea animal that holds to ships, rocks, and logs.

bar'ri er (băr'ĭ ẽr). 1. A gate or bar that marks the start of a race. 2. A fence or anything of the sort that serves to keep out or separate.

bee'tle (bē't'l). An insect with four wings. The outer pair are stiff cases which cover the others when folded.

Bel ler'o phon (bĕ lĕr'ō fŏn). A Greek hero who killed the monster called the Chimera.

bi'son (bī's'n). The American buffalo. It is a large animal with a big shaggy head, short horns, and a hump.

bleat (blēt). To make the cry of a sheep or lamb.

boom (bo͞om). A chain of floating logs to hold other logs together.

Boone, Dan'iel (bo͞on, dăn'yĕl). An American woodsman who led the way over the mountains into Kentucky and beyond.

---

lāte, ăm, färm, ȧsk, câre, wē, wĕt, lettẽr, hīde, hĭd, ōld, nŏt, hôrse, sŏft, ūse, ŭs, bûrn, mo͞on, fo͝ot, oil, out

Bos′ton (bŏs′tŭn). The capital of the state of Massachusetts.

bough (bou). A branch of a tree.

bri′dle (brī′d′l). The straps which fit over a horse's head and the bit and lines by which the rider controls him.

bris′tly (brĭs′lĭ). Having sharp points or bristles like a brush.

buck (bŭk). 1. To spring upward with the head held down. 2. The male of deer, goats, hares, or rabbits.

bur′ro (bûr′ō). A donkey of southwestern United States.

C

cac′tus (kăk′tŭs). A kind of plant with fleshy stem and branches, covered with scales or needles instead of leaves. It can grow in very dry soil.

Cal i for′ni a (kăl ĭ fôr′nĭ à). The state farthest southwest in the United States.

car′bu ret or (kär′bū rĕt′ẽr). That part of a motor which mixes air with gasoline vapor.

cau′tious ly (kô′shŭs lĭ). Very carefully, as if on the lookout for danger.

Chi ca′go (shĭ kô′gō). A large city in the state of Illinois.

Chi me′ra (kī mē′rà). A dragon-like monster in Greek stories.

chis′el (chĭz″l). 1. A tool with a sharp edge at one end. 2. To cut with a chisel.

chuck′le (chŭk″l). 1. To laugh quietly. 2. A low, quiet laugh.

Chuk′luk (chŭk′lŭk).

Clin′ton, De Witt′ (klĭn′tŭn, dē wĭt′). 1. The name given to an early American locomotive. 2. A famous governor of New York State.

cock a lo′rum (kŏk à lō′rŭm). Master of All Masters' name for fire.

col′o ny (kŏl′ō nĭ). 1. A group of birds of the same kind living close together. 2. A group of people who have moved from their mother country to a new land.

com′pound (kŏm′pound). Made of two or more like parts put together.

con tent′ed (kŏn tĕn′tĕd). Happy with whatever one has.

con tract′ (kŏn trăkt′). 1. To become smaller; to grow narrow; to draw together. 2. To agree to do something.

crag (krăg). 1. A rock that stands out in a point on high ground. 2. A rough cliff.

Cu′ba (kū′bà). A large island in the Atlantic Ocean off the southeast coast of the United States.

cud (kŭd). Partly chewed food which a cow brings up from her first stomach to be chewed again.

Cum'ber land Gap (kŭm'bẽr-lănd găp). A pass through the mountains from Virginia to Kentucky and Tennessee.

Cumberland Road. The first road built at government expense. It ran from Cumberland, Maryland, to the Ohio River.

cu ri os'i ty (kū rĭ ŏs'ĭ tĭ). 1. An eager wish to know. 2. Something strange.

cut'worm (kŭt'wûrm). A caterpillar that cuts off young plants near the ground.

D

dab'ble (dăb''l). To splash and spatter; to paddle in the water.

Di e'go (dē ā'gō).

dit'ty (dĭt'ĭ). A short, simple poem or song.

dog'wood (dŏg'wŏŏd). · A kind of flowering tree or bush.

Doo'dy (dōō'dĭ).

drain'pipe (drān'pīp). A pipe through which water and waste mat ter flow away.

dusk (dŭsk). 1. The half darkness just before night. 2. Gloom.

E

ear'nest ly (ûr'nĕst lĭ). Eagerly and with much interest. A person who is in earnest is serious and not playful.

em broi'dered (ĕm broi'dẽrd). Decorated with needlework.

Eng'land (ĭng'glănd). A country in the islands northwest of Europe.

Eng'lish (ĭng'glĭsh). 1. Of, or coming from, England. 2. The people of England. 3. The language of the people of Great Britain and of the United States.

en tan'gled (ĕn tăng'g'ld). Held fast or trapped by twisted threads or cords.

etched (ĕcht). Drew clear sharp lines as if cut by acid on metal.

ex cur'sion (ĕks kûr'zhŭn). A trip made chiefly for fun and a good time.

F

Fe ra'gi (fĕ rä'zhĕ).

fer'ry (fĕr'ĭ). 1. A boat that carries people or things across a river. 2. A place where something is carried by boat across a river. 3. To carry persons or things across a river.

---

jāte, ăm, färm. àsk, câre, wē, wĕt, lettẽr, hīde, hĭd, ōld, nŏt, hôrse, sŏft, ūse, ŭs, bûrn, mōon, fŏŏt, oil, out

Finland

Fin'land (fĭn'lănd). A country in northern Europe between Sweden and Russia.

flick'er (flĭk'ẽr). To burn unsteadily; to grow bright and die away.

Flor'i da (flŏr'ĭ dà). The state farthest southeast in the United States.

flu'id (floo͞'ĭd). Something that can flow like water.

flung (flŭng). Threw with force.

Fran'co (fräng'kō).

freight (frāt). 1. A load carried by boat or train. 2. A train carrying goods. 3. The money paid for the carrying of goods.

Fuad (fwăd).

G

grace'ful (grās'fŏol). Displaying beauty in form and action.

graze (grāz). To feed on grass and other growing things.

Greece (grēs). A country of southeastern Europe.

Gre'tel (grā'tĕl). A girl in a fairy tale.

grub (grŭb). A soft, wormlike creature which grows into a beetle or other insect.

guard (gärd). 1. To watch over and protect from danger. 2. The act of watching and protecting. 3. A person who protects.

gull (gŭl). A kind of web-footed water bird with long wings.

H

hang'ar (hăng'ẽr). A building in which airplanes are kept.

Han'sel (hăn'sĕl). A boy in a fairy tale.

haunt'ed (hônt'ĕd). Visited often, especially by ghosts.

home'ly (hōm'lĭ). Not beautiful or handsome.

hon'or (ŏn'ẽr). 1. A title given to show respect. 2. To look up to, as one of special importance.

horse'-rad'ish (hôrs'-răd'ĭsh). 1. A white-flowered plant. 2. Hot-tasting sauce, made from the root of the plant, to be eaten with meat.

hud'dled (hŭd''ld). 1. Drawn up into a heap. 2. Crowded together.

Hud'son, Hen'ry (hŭd's'n, hĕn'rĭ). An English explorer who discovered the American river named for him.

hum'ble (hŭm'b'l). 1. Simple and plain. 2. Not proud.

Hun'ga ry (hŭng'ga rĭ). A country in Central Europe.

hurl (hûrl). To throw hard; to fling.

hy e'na (hī ē'nà). A large, strong, meat-eating animal of

438

Asia and Africa that hunts by night.

I

ice'berg (īs'bûrg). A large, floating mass of ice.

In'di a (ĭn'dĭ à). A country of southern Asia.

J

Jai (jī).

Jan'csi (yŏn'chĭ).

jig'sawed (jĭg'sôd). Cut in curved lines like a jigsaw puzzle; therefore, much puzzled.

John Bull (jŏn bŏŏl). 1. The name of an early English locomotive. 2. A nickname for England and Englishmen.

K

Ka'sha (kä'shä).

ken'nel (kĕn'ĕl). 1. A house for a dog or dogs. 2. A place where dogs are raised for sale.

Ken tuck'y (kĕn tŭk'ĭ). A state of the Middle West just south of the Ohio River.

kin'dle (kĭn'd'l). To set on fire; to light.

Kin'tu (kĭn'tōō).

Ki tom'ba (kĭ tŏm'bà).

ko a'la (kō ä'là or kōō'là). A small animal that lives in trees in Australia. It looks like a Teddy bear.

L

land'scape (lănd'skāp). 1. A stretch of land which the eyes can cover at a glance. 2. A painting or other picture of a scene.

lard'er (lär'dẽr). A place where food is kept.

ledge (lĕj). A shelf of rock; a flat piece sticking out from a wall.

lit'ter (lĭt'ẽr). 1. The young animals born all at one time to a dog or other animal. 2. Things lying around in disorder. 3. Straw or hay used as bedding for animals.

lo co mo'tive (lō kō mō'tĭv). An engine that moves under its own power and is usually used to pull railroad cars.

looped (lōōpt). Made in the form of a loop or ring.

loop'hole (lōōp'hōl). A small opening in a wall, through which a gun can be fired.

lye (lī). A strong fluid made from putting water through wood ashes.

M

Ma gel'lan (mà jĕl'ăn). 1. The name of a monkey. 2. An early explorer who was killed

---

lāte, ăm, färm, àsk, câre, wē, wĕt, lettẽr, hīde, hĭd, ōld, nŏt, hôrse, sŏft, ūse, ŭs, bûrn, mōōn, fŏŏt, oil, out in the Philippine Islands. His ship was the first to sail around the world.

Maine (mān). The state farthest northeast in the United States.

Ma′ki (mă′kĭ).

Ma nu el′ (mä no͝o ĕl′).

Math′ew, Da′vid (măth′ū, dā′-vĭd). A man who was engineer of little Blacknose.

Mex′i co (mĕk′sĭ kō). A country just south of the United States

mil′li ner (mĭl′ĭ nẽr). One who makes or sells hats for women.

Mim′kin (mĭm′kĭn).

min′er al (mĭn′ẽr ăl). Something in nature that is neither animal nor plant nor their remains. Many rocks are minerals.

Moo′loo (mo͞o′lo͞o).

mos qui′to (mŭs kē′tō). A small insect with two wings. It stings men and animals and draws out blood.

munch (mŭnch). To chew with a grinding sound.

Mur rie′ta, Joa quin′ (mo͞or ryā′-tä, wä kēn′). A bandit of olden days in California.

mus′ket (mŭs′kĕt). An old kind of gun fired with a match or matchlock.

N

Nagy (nŏj).

neigh (nā). 1. The cry of a horse. 2. To give the cry of a horse.

440

Nin′ya (nēn′yä).

ni′pa (nē′pȧ). A kind of palm tree that grows in the Philippines. The leaves are used in building houses.

nought (nôt). Nothing.

O

o be′di ence (ō bē′dĭ ĕns). The act of obeying.

O hi′o (ō hī′ō). 1. A state in the Middle West of the United States. 2. A large river of the United States.

P

Pa cif′ic (pȧ sĭf′ĭk). The largest ocean of the world. It lies between western America and eastern Asia.

palm (päm). 1. The inside of the hand. 2. A useful tree of the tropics. Several kinds are the coconut palm, the date palm, the nipa palm, and the royal palm.

pan ta loons′ (păn tȧ lo͞onz′). Old-fashioned trousers.

pass′port (pȧs′pōrt). A letter giving one the right to go from one place to another, especially outside one's own country.

patch′work (păch′wûrk). Something made of patches or pieces, often of different colors and sizes.

peer (pēr). To look carefully and curiously.

Peg'a sus (pĕg'á sŭs). A horse with wings, told about in old Greek stories.

pest (pĕst). 1. Anything, such as an animal or insect, which annoys and causes damage. 2. A sickness which spreads quickly and kills many people.

Phil'ip pine Is'lands (fĭl'ĭ pēn ī'lăndz). A group of islands southeast of Asia.

plan ta'tion (plăn tā'shŭn). A place planted to a special crop, such as sugar cane or cotton, and using many field workers.

pon da lo'rum (pŏn dá lō'rŭm). Master of All Masters' name for water.

por'ter (pōr'tẽr). 1. One who works in sleeping cars or other special cars on a train. 2. One who carries packages and baggage for pay.

prompt'ly (prŏmpt'lĭ). At once; quickly.

Pug'wug (pŭg'wŭg).

Q

quay (kē). A landing place, often of stone, for loading and unloading boats; a wharf.

quiv'er (kwĭv'ẽr). 1. To shake or shiver, usually from excitement. 2. A case for carrying arrows.

R

race'course (rās'kōrs). A track or route for a race.

reed (rēd). A kind of tall grass, often with a jointed stem.

re mark'a ble (rē mär'ká b'l). Unusual; so different as to be noticed.

re serve' (rē zûrv'). To set aside for special use.

ridge (rĭj). A row of hills or mountains.

ring'mas ter (rĭng'más tẽr). The man in charge of the different acts in the circus rings.

roach (rōch). A fresh-water fish with a greenish back.

Rog'ers (rŏj'ẽrz).

Ron'ka (rŏn'kä).

rough (rŭf). 1. Not smooth. 2. Not gentle. 3. Unfinished.

route (rōōt). A road or way that is to be traveled, as on a trip.

roy'al (roi'ăl). Suited to a king.

rud'dy (rŭd'ĭ). Reddish in color.

Rus'sian (rŭsh'ăn). Of Russia, a large country in northern Europe and Asia.

---

lāte, ăm, färm, ȧsk, câre, wē, wĕt, lettẽr, hīde, hĭd, ōld, nŏt, hôrse, sŏft, ūse, ŭs, bûrn, mōon, fŏŏt, oil, out

S

sag (săg). To sink in the middle.

San Joa quin' (săn wä kēn'). A river and valley in California.

Sche nec'ta dy (skĕ nĕk'tȧ dĭ). A city in the state of New York.

screech (skrēch). To make a high, sharp cry; to shriek.

sea'soned (sē'z'nd). Dried and hardened, ready for use; as seasoned wood.

Se ñor' (sā nyôr'). 1. Spanish word for *gentleman.* 2. A title meaning *Mr.* or *Sir.*

Se ñor'a (sā nyō'rä). 1. Spanish word for *lady.* 2. A title meaning *Mrs.* or *Madam.*

Se ño ri'ta (sā nyō rē'tä). 1. Spanish word for *young lady.* 2. A title meaning *Miss.*

ser'geant (sär'jĕnt). A police officer next below a captain.

show'boat (shō'bōt). A steamboat, part of which is used for showing movies or giving plays.

Sim'i ny (sĭm'ĭ nĭ).

snarl (snärl). 1. A snapping growl. 2. To growl with a snap of the teeth.

sped (spĕd). Moved very fast; went with speed.

Splop (splŏp).

squibs (skwĭbz) **and crackers.** Master of All Masters' name for his trousers.

stam pede' (stăm pēd'). 1. To run away wildly, as a herd of animals in fright. 2. A wild running away, as of animals.

stead'fast (stĕd'fȧst). Not changing; steady; firm.

stream'line (strēm'līn). Having a shape and surface so smooth that air flows around it easily.

stride (strīd). 1. A long, regular step 2. To walk or run with long, regular steps.

strut (strŭt). 1. To walk proudly. 2. A proud walk.

sun'shade (sŭn'shād). Anything used to keep off the light and heat of the sun.

Sven (svĕn).

swan (swŏn). A large water bird, usually white, with a very long neck.

swish (swĭsh). 1. To move with a sound like a whip cutting the air. 2. A soft sound like that of a silk skirt.

T

Tau'no (tou'nō).

temp ta'tion (tĕmp tā'shŭn). 1. Anything which tempts, or leads, one to do wrong. 2. The state of being led into wrongdoing.

ter'ri er (tĕr'ĭ ẽr). A kind of dog, small, smart, brave, and lively.

thun'der bolt (thŭn'dẽr bōlt). 1. A flash of lightning and clap

442

of thunder. 2. Something sudden and frightening.

tim'id (tĭm'ĭd). Not brave; feeling or showing fear.

toll (tōl). A tax paid for a certain reason, such as using a road or bridge.

tor'toise (tôr'tŭs). A turtle, especially a land turtle.

To'ta ram (tō'tä räm).

tour'ist (tŏor'ĭst). One who travels for the fun of it.

trans par'ent (trăns pâr'ĕnt). Clear like window glass so that objects beyond can be seen.

tra peze' (tră pēz'). A short pole hung by ropes tied to either end, and used for swinging and doing tricks in the air.

trudge (trŭj). To walk steadily but wearily.

U

un'der growth (ŭn'dĕr grōth). That which grows under trees; small plants and bushes in a forest.

U nit'ed States (ū nīt'ĕd stāts). The forty-eight states of North America, which form a republic.

U'tah (ū'tô). A state in western United States.

V

Val en ti'na (vä lĕn tē'nä).

W

wal'let (wŏl'ĕt). 1. A pocketbook. 2. A bag or sack for carrying things on a trip.

Wash'ing ton (wŏsh'ĭng tŭn). 1. The state farthest northwest in the United States. 2. The capital of the United States. 3. The first President of the United States.

Way Ping (wā pĭng).

webbed (wĕbd). Having web, or skin, between the toes, as many water birds have.

Wednes'day (wĕnz'dĭ). The fourth day of the week.

whine (hwīn). 1. To make a low crying sound as if in trouble. 2. A low, begging sound.

whir (hwûr). 1. To move with a whizzing sound. 2. A buzzing sound.

wire'worm (wīr'wûrm). A thin caterpillar with a hard skin, which becomes a beetle.

with'ered (wĭth'ĕrd). Dried, faded, and wrinkled.

Wud'dle (wŭd'l).

Y

yah hya ris (yä hī rĭs). Words of a shepherds' song in North Africa.

yield (yēld). 1. To give up; to give way to. 2. To bear fruit.

---

lāte, ăm, färm, ȧsk, câre, wē, wĕt, lettẽr, hīde, hĭd, ōld, nŏt, hôrse, sŏft, ūse, ŭs, bûrn, mo͞on, fo͝ot, oil, out

To the Teacher

This Fourth Reader, *Roads to Everywhere*, follows *Friends Far and Near*, the Third Reader, Level II, of the GINN BASIC READING SERIES.

This Fourth Reader introduces 696 new words, and, exclusive of proper names, maintains 97 per cent of the words taught in all the earlier books of this series.

In the book there are a few foreign words (see "Your Dictionary," pp. 434–443) and words in dialect. These are not included in the count of new words.

New words which occur only in the poetry are starred. Except for starred words, not more than four new words appear on any page.

New Words in This Book

9 daring
deeds
10 explorer
Rex
11 . . .
12 foolish
pressed
button
13 stream
14 settled
twinkling
15 gazed
whining
16 footprints
person
17 . . .
18 terribly
midnight
yell
rescue
19 . . .
20 . . .
21 echo
22 chips
museum
23 jolly
case
*beef
chest

24 whether
*iceberg
25 Janie's
cabin
26 Ohio
ridge
27 bar
musket
fault
28 cradle
loophole
frosted
29 . . .
30 whirring
whoop
31 sleeve
powder
32 teapot
Boston
dainty
church
33 shrieking
34 . . .
35 . . .
36 . . .
37 Sven's
bunk
mad
teasing

38 jokes
scarf
rough
39 float
showboat
Hanson's
movies
40 dabbling
boom
stealing
motor
41 already
stern
swung
42 bay
43 meant
flung
44 dipped
bail
forward
Kemp's
45 gleam
46 . . .
47 . . .
48 laughter
slept
49 Becky
bandit
Papa

50 Simon's
trousers
51 San Joaquin
tax
52 Murrieta
53 . . .
54 spoke
Prince
creek
55 shivering
56 galloped
fear
57 bridle
58 . . .
59 disliked
drew
60 . . .
61 Hudson's
sir
Henry
crew
62 nodded
discovering
India
63 row
64 taught
anchored
65 difference

444

445

447

385 unblinking
cushion
386 carrot
*fringed
*beet
387 nonsense
388 Kasha
Ronka
Ninya
Russian
389 . . .
390 annoyed
skirt
embroidered
blouse
391 timid
392 cud
393 . . .
394 . . .
395 rug

396 . . .
397 fifth
398 promptly
399 . . .
400 judge
honor
allow
bid
401 . . .
402 smothered
403 . . .
404 . . .
405 hire
pantaloons
barnacle
406 squibs
Siminy
407 cockalorum
pondalorum
408 . . .

409 *entangled
410 Wuddle
factory
Doody
411 strutted
Splop
Mooloo
412 squawked
butted
Mimkin
Pugwug
413 . . .
414 Chukluk
growled
415 . . .
416 aches
pains
417 . . .
418 exclaimed

419 pests
420 damage
plow
lawn
421 lame
422 clip
423 . . .
424 . . .
425 . . .
426 . . .
427 jigsawed
puzzle
428 . . .
429 horse-radish
430 . . .
431 . . .
432 . . .
433 . . .

PRINTED IN THE UNITED STATES OF AMERICA